F

C000130637

The People's History

Bridges of the River Wear

by

Keith Cockerill

For Joan, Anthony and Graeme

Previous page: Wolsingham or Wear's Bridge, erected in 1894.

Copyright © Keith Cockerill 2005

First published in 2005 by

The People's History Ltd
Suite 1, Byron House
Seaham Grange Business Park, Seaham
County Durham SR7 0PY

ISBN: 1 902527 34 8

No part of this publication may be reproduced, stored in a mechanical retrieval system, or transmitted, in any form or by any means, electronic, mechanical, photocopying, recording or otherwise, without prior permission of the author.

Foreword

In May of 1796 my ancestor John Cockerill 'mariner of Scarborough' married Jane Thekstone of Kendal in the bustling port of Sunderland. Some three months later the largest single span cast iron bridge in the world was unveiled to the people of the town. If John was not away at sea, then perhaps he was amongst the 80,000 spectators who witnessed this grand occasion and marvelled at one of the engineering wonders of the age.

By the mid 19th century my forebears were shipowners and master mariners in the port. In 1849 the shipyard of William Robinson launched the 377 ton bark *Cockerills* for John's eldest son Anthony. Family vessels were not only working in the coastal coal trade at this time, but also sailing to far away places such as the Mediterranean and Canada. In the winter of 1852, my great-great-grandfather Anthony Jnr came to the assistance of a young lady when she slipped on the icy steps of the Sunderland Ferry. They were to marry within weeks. He died 'on the high seas' in 1867 whilst master of a family vessel which was sailing from Hamburg to Sunderland.

Family-owned ships must have sailed under the Wearmouth Bridge of 1796 and its successor of 1859 on many occasions. Subsequent generations of the family in Sunderland would maintain links with the sea as boat builders and shipyard workers in the town. They will have crossed the Wearmouth Bridge of 1929 many times on their way to the shipyards on both sides of the river.

I recount the above family history to explain my interest in the bridges and ferries of Sunderland and the germination of an idea to photograph all of the structures over the river. I have no doubt that the reader whose ancestors have also lived and worked by the Wear will be able to relate their own and perhaps very different family history to the river and its bridges.

In August of 2004, I stood by the 'Win Pool' at Wearhead to witness the rise of the River Wear. Here I contemplated the second phase of the project: to research the history of each bridge that I had photographed. This book is the outcome of both ventures.

One of the mid span crests that adorn the rails at each side of Wearmouth Bridge bearing the words of Sunderland's motto: 'Nil desperandum auspice deo'.

Acknowledgements

Raymond Selkirk, Peter Bowes, David Archer, Robert Major, Ron Henderson, David Twinn, Frank Walton, Marion Holmes, Ann Wilkinson, Stan Bell, John Bartlett, Tom Hutchinson, Michael F. Richardson, Dawn Cummings, Alan Vickers, Alan Plews, Sheila Hogarth, Chris Lloyd, Les Blackett, Bryan Chambers and Bob Abley.

> The Weardale Gazette
> Witton Park History Group
> South Hylton Local History Society
> The Lambton Estate
> www.geocities.com/waggonways
> www.weardale-railway.org.uk/history.htm
> David Simpson's North East England History Pages
> www.thenortheast.fsnet.co.uk

Bibliography

Chester-le-Street And Its Place In History by Raymond Selkirk 2001
Picturesque Weardale by W.M. Eggleston 1916. North of England Newspaper Co Ltd
Picturesque Weardale Revisited by Peter Bowes 1996. Weardale Publishing and Printing Co Ltd
History, Topography and Directory of Durham 1894
Some Chapters on the History of Sunderland by Helen G. Bowling 1969
History of Sunderland by W.C. Mitchell. Published by E.J. Morten 1919 & 1972
Durham City and the Railway Age by Alan Maitland. County Durham Books 1995
Along The Line and Over The Wear an article by D. Fairer 1960
Memories of Witton Park by Gillian Wales and R. McManus
Durham – The People and the Place 1914-1939 by Michael F. Richardson 1994
Durham – Historic and University City by Margot Johnson, MA, FLA 1987
The North Eastern Railway, Its Rise and Development by W.W. Tomlinson 1914
The New Wearmouth Bridge, Sunderland A paper by Geoffrey Lancaster Groves BSc, M Inst CE

The three bridges at Witton Park before the removal of the footbridge. Courtesy of Witton Park History Group.

Bridges of the River Wear

The Burnhope and Killhope Burns converge in the Pennines at the westerly edge of County Durham, with the River Wear rising at the point of their union to grant the name of Wearhead to the small village that exists nearby. From high in the Pennine moors, the newly formed river gaining in force and strength flows south easterly past Ireshopeburn, St John's Chapel, Westgate, Eastgate, Stanhope and Frosterley – the sheep farming, quarrying and former mining communities of Weardale. Having fallen some 600 feet over the first part of its journey, onwards it flows to the rolling hills of Wolsingham, passing Witton-le-Wear, Witton Park and Escombe before reaching the market town of Bishop Auckland. Here it alters course to head north east past the old coal mining communities of Hunwick and Newfield, then onwards via Willington, Sunderland Bridge and Shincliffe towards the City of Durham. After its majestic loop around the peninsula that carries the magnificent Norman Cathedral of Durham, it runs down to the old Roman fort town of Chester-le-Street. At this juncture it signals its intention to head more directly for the North Sea via the Lambton Estate, Washington and Hylton. Just as Wearhead received its name from the birth of the river, so its final search for the North Sea created the township names at its mouth. Monkwearmouth, and the land gifted to its 7th century monks on the opposite side of the water but separated or sundered by the river: Sunderland.

For as long as people have lived along the 67 miles of the Wear, there will have existed a necessity to cross or navigate it. In the upper reaches of the river

The rise of the River Wear at the confluence of the Killhope (left) and Burnhope (right) Burns. The Wearhead Bridge of 1989 stands in the background.

The site of the dam at Hylton which is thought by the Northern Archaeology Group to be Roman in date.

where it is narrow and shallow, natural flat rock could easily have been positioned by the early dwellers for stepping-stones and rough fords created at shallow points for cattle and carts. For deeper and wider channels further downstream, wooden craft will have been utilised. A 4,000 year-old dug-out canoe discovered on the riverbed at Hylton in 1885 provides very early evidence of this.

Following extensive research, the Northern Archaeology Group has suggested that when the Romans arrived, they created a series of dams along the River Wear or Vedra Fluvius as they called it to make it navigable upstream, possibly as far as Bishop Auckland. The group is of the opinion that the river became a major supply route for the Roman army. The Romans first weir, a massive 10 feet high structure, is thought to have been constructed at Hylton. This would have enabled the huge quantity of supplies and provisions that they required to be brought upstream to Hylton in merchant ships, then transferred onto barges to be taken further upriver to their fort at Chester-le-Street.

Binchester Fort near Bishop Auckland is said to be the Roman fort of Vinovia constructed in the late 1st and early 2nd centuries, possibly to protect a bridge of stone and timber construction over the Wear. This bridge sat on the line of Dere Street, the main Roman road north from York to Scotland. However, a bridge demolished in 1388 on the site of the nearby 14th century Newton Cap Bridge is also said to have been of Roman origin and this has created debate as to the actual siting of Vinovia and the line of Dere Street itself. Roman bridges may have also existed by the site of the modern Page Bank Bridge near Whitworth Hall and the Roman fort in Chester-le-Street. Two other possible Roman bridges are associated with Durham, one on the river below Kepier medieval hospital and a wooden structure in old Durham. Fords at Stanhope and Tudhoe are also said to date from this period.

When the Romans left the county in the early part of the 5th century, they took their engineering skills with them. Over 700 years would elapse before the stone bridges around the city of Durham were constructed. As old Roman roadway systems were further developed, new strategic crossing points would have materialised along the river and numerous tolled ferries and fords developed around them. The remains of an Anglo-Saxon ford and chapel exist downstream of the 15th century bridge at Chester-le-Street, parts of which are still said to be visible today at low tide.

Many of the fords over the Wear date to the early medieval period and some are still in use around Weardale. As native expertise evolved, however, the skills of bridge building were again slowly rediscovered. These early bridges were undoubtedly made of wood and probably built on the sites of old fords, but by the middle of the 12th century in Norman County Durham grand stone arched bridges were also being erected across the river. Many of the bridges of this period were conceived and financed by religious leaders. Some of the Wear's medieval stone bridges such as Bishop Skirlaw's Bridge are still in use today.

By the end of the 18th century, new materials were being considered for the construction of bridges. In 1796 the great cast iron bridge at Sunderland was opened, the largest single span cast iron bridge in the world and only the second structure to make use of this material. 'The stupendous structure looks light and woven, like the spiders' meshes which that insect has spun in the air

Huntshield Ford in Weardale, said to date to the 12th century and still in use today.

The great Cast Iron Bridge of 1796 at Sunderland.

across some vast chasm' wrote visitor Dr Augustus Granville in 1841. Wrought iron and steel were utilised after this in bridge building to replace the more fragile cast iron material.

The development of the railways in the North East created the need for a new type of river crossing – the rail bridge. Most over the Wear were constructed throughout the 19th century. Wooden rail bridges were erected on colliery wagonways in the 1840s to carry coals across the Wear and five of these are thought to have existed on a short stretch of the river between Newfield and Willington. However, it is the grand stone viaducts and iron rail bridges that have survived as a lasting tribute to the Victorian engineers who designed and built them. The viaduct at Croxdale is still in use for main line rail traffic, but others now lie abandoned. The immense Newton Cap Viaduct at Bishop Auckland has in recent times been converted into a road bridge. Its commemorative plaque bears the inscription 'viaducts will endure for ages'. It is pleasing to see that some of the 19th century iron rail bridges in Weardale are now being brought back into use, as steam enthusiasts open up part of the historic Weardale line between Stanhope and Wolsingham.

As quarries and mines were developed in County Durham, workmen needed to cross the river regularly to get to their place of work. Fords were not always reliable and were sometimes dangerous in times of flood. Around the end of the 19th century at least three suspension bridges were erected over the Wear for the use of miners and quarrymen. These footbridges were either built by the men themselves or from funds raised by public subscription and were sited at Frosterley, Escombe and Belmont.

Most of the road bridges now spanning the River Wear are not the original structures on the site. Many have been widened, altered or replaced to meet the needs of modern transport. Records show the Wear to be prone to flooding and many flash floods over the centuries are known to have caused irreparable damage to them. Flood levels or 'height of fresh' are sometimes recorded on bridges, as for example on the Victoria Viaduct at Penshaw. Weardale has suffered badly over the years in terms of flood damage and many of its picturesque stone arched bridges and wooden footbridges have needed strengthening, repair, or replacement.

Increasing traffic congestion now dictates the siting, planning and erection of new bridges. Traffic flow through the City of Durham was vastly improved by the construction of two new road bridges in the 1960s and '70s to protect the historic heart of the city and its old bridges. A new £40 million bridge has been proposed for a site upstream of Sunderland's Queen Alexandra Bridge around the Claxheugh area. In 2002 world famous architect Frank Gehry visited the city to discuss the possibility of designing it. The reclamation of land from the old Wearmouth Colliery and construction of the Stadium of Light football ground has raised the possibility of a new footbridge being built between the stadium and a new development on the former Vaux brewery complex.

Many an amateur photographer including myself cannot resist pointing his camera at a bridge and water. I hope I have been able to capture just a tiny fragment of the beauty of the River Wear and its bridges. My photographs and accompanying text start at Wearhead at the rise of the Wear and show each bridge or crossing in downstream order as the river makes its drive for the North Sea at Sunderland. Where appropriate, archive photographs have been included. Each bridge photographed fully spans the River Wear. The many bridges of its tributaries I'm afraid must wait for another day.

The river arch of the Victoria Viaduct. Flood levels are recorded on the inner side of the right hand pillar.

Wearhead Bridge

Wearhead Bridge has the distinction of being the first bridge to face the waters of the Wear and stands just downstream of the river's rise at the confluence of the Killhope and Burnhope Burns. A stone bridge of two arches was constructed here in 1768. It is recorded that in 1801, a gentleman by the name of John Shields jumped the battlements at a gallop and 'neither the horse nor its rider was any worse'. It was thought, however, to be a dangerous bridge for the conventional user, as a sharp turn at the south end of the structure was the cause of many accidents. The bridge was said to be more suitable for packhorse use than carts, and was consequently widened in 1810 when an additional arch was erected adjacent to the original. The stone bridge was replaced by an iron bridge in 1889, which compared to its predecessor, was perhaps not quite so pleasing to the eye. The iron bridge suffered flood damage in the late 1980s and a scheme for its replacement was instigated.

In 1989 Durham County Council in its centenary year, erected a modern twin reinforced concrete bridge of two arches, which when clad with natural stone brought the former splendour of the old stone arched bridge back to the village of Wearhead. Its designer was the Director of the Environment, D.J. Newbegin MSc, CEng, FICE, FIHT. The Chairman of the County Council, Councillor, Jim Graham formally opened the bridge on 11th September 1989.

The area of water where the Killhope and Burnhope Burns meet is called the Wine or Win Pool. Its name comes from the Anglo-Saxon 'winn' meaning a contest or struggle, which aptly describes the interaction between the two burns before they finally unite to form the River Wear.

The Wine or Win Pool at the rise of the river. Wearhead Bridge is just downsteam.

Sparks Farm Bridge, Wearhead

Some 300 yards downstream of Wearhead village, a small private bridge is situated at Sparks Farm that gives access to its property on both sides of the river. It effectively connects two adjoining areas of land belonging to the farm, so animals can easily be moved from one field to another.

The present bridge was erected in 1986 by Robsons of Allendale (Allenheads). It is a two span metal beam bridge on natural stone

Sparks Farm Bridge of 1986.

abutments and centre pier, with timber decking and tubular rails. It replaced a previous bridge that had been in service for around 40 years until it collapsed when a tractor was driven across it.

Blackdene Bridge, West Blackdene

Weardale Naturalists Field Club on an outing to Blackdene Bridge.

Blackdene Bridge was built in 1848 to connect the village to Ireshopeburn. The natural stone structure of two arches stands proudly at the head of the village in a beautiful tranquil setting and water flows under the bridge to spill downstream through a chain of small cascading waterfalls. The row of 19th century miners' cottages adjacent to the river sits in perfect harmony with the scene. Slightly downstream, old mine buildings are now being renovated to create new homes for the community.

The village has not always benefited from this quiet rural charm, for it took the closure and demolition (1981 to 1997) of the nearby Blackdene Mine to create it. An ever-increasing level of associated industrial traffic had used the old stone structure before the erection of a dedicated mine bridge a quarter of a mile downstream. In addition the tall processing plant of 1978 generated an unflattering backdrop for the village, but it was eventually demolished to the great satisfaction of the residents.

In July 1983 the bridge was badly damaged by flooding and a nearby building had a much swollen burn flowing over its roof.

Blackdene Mine Bridge

This is a bridge that now leads to nowhere but it was erected to serve the fluorspar and lead mine of Blackdene when it was in full production. Hardly any trace of the mine now exists and the site has been fully restored to a condition where it is now capable of being used as agricultural pastureland. The bridge is modern in design and construction and is thought to have been erected around 1978 after Nationalisation took place and the mine had passed into the hands of British Steel. There are indications around the site that an older river structure may have once existed here. These are likely to be the remains of the 'Jinn Wheel', which once harnessed the power of the river for use in the mining process.

The mine was driven into the hillside from the banks of the River Wear to tap into the Blackdene vein, but mining is first mentioned in the area as early as 1401 when Roger Thornton was granted permission to work a mine at Aldwoodclough. By 1818, 26,581 tons of lead concentrates were being

processed. An aqueduct is shown crossing the river near the site of the crushing mill on a mid 19th century map. In 1905-06, five tons of lead and 43 tons of fluorspar were produced at the mine. It was taken over by United Steel Co in 1949 when it was rigorously developed and by

Blackdene Mine Bridge at 'The Jinn Pool'.

1953 its output was 6,500 tons per year. In 1967 the business passed to British Steel but by 1981 production had ceased at the mine and eleven years later it was put into receivership. By 1997 the mine site was completely cleared but the bridge was left intact. The area around the bridge, known locally as 'The Jinn Pool', is now a popular spot for fishing and Weardale House runs a canoeing course here for its students.

Coronation Bridge

This handsome stone bridge of two arches was erected half a mile downstream of Ireshopeburn, the foundation stone being laid on the day of the Coronation of Queen Victoria hence the name that it was given. It is reported that the bridge gave way when built and had to be re-constructed the following year, when 'some pieces of money were deposited in the foundations for luck'. The arches of the bridge are elliptical in shape and the structure being narrow is absent of a footpath.

The bridge was considered to be of great importance at this time, as the local lead mine and repair shops of W.B. Beaumont were located to the north side of the bridge at Newhouse. Before the building of the bridge, it is said that the ford here was deep and difficult to negotiate. When agents brought the pay for the miners at the lead mine, water often touched the saddlebags of their horses as they crossed the river. Another account reports that a fish was once found on the floor of a carriage after it had crossed the ford!

A pillar of the bridge was seriously damaged in the flood of 9th March 1881, when a day of heavy rainfall followed a sudden thaw of deep snow.

In September 2000 Durham County Council strengthened the bridge to make it suitable for modern day traffic. It was given a reinforced concrete saddle to enable it to carry 40 tonne 'Euro lorries'.

Coronation Bridge, first erected in 1838.

Bridge End Ford and Footbridge

Bridge End Ford is situated in Middle Blackdene some 400 yards downstream of the Coronation Bridge. It sits at the end of a track off the A689 that leads to the river at Pennine Lodge. The ford is a natural one consisting of shelves of block limestone that stretch across almost the full width of the river and water cascades away from the crossing via a small waterfall. The ford provided the only access to High House and beyond until the erection of Coronation Bridge in 1838. A footbridge of metal construction and concrete decking exists just

downstream of the ford which was erected in the late 1940s or early '50s. An earlier wooden footbridge stood here however in 1916. Access to the present bridge from the south side is gained via the rear garden of Pennine Lodge. Middle Blackdene was the site of an early lead mine called 'Old Faw', the word faw meaning field.

Above: The southern approach to Bridge End Ford at Middle Blackdene.

Left: Bridge End Footbridge, built late 1940s/early '50s.

Broken Way Ford and Footbridge

Broken Way Ford and Footbridge are situated at the western edge of the village of St John's Chapel. The crossing is named after an ancient rough track for horse and carts which linked Burnfoot on the south side of the river to East Blackdene on the north side, long before the construction of the modern A689.

When the railways arrived in St John's Chapel around 1895 a single arch rail bridge was erected over Broken Way adjacent to the ford, so the river crossing would still appear to have been of strategic importance at this time. Today the overgrown nature of the approach path on the south side and the reinforcement of the riverbank on the north side suggest that this is no longer a ford that is in use.

In 1861 the river crossing was still complemented by a set of stepping-stones for foot users, but a wooden footbridge was eventually constructed downstream of the ford, perhaps towards the end of the 19th century. In August of 1985 a bridge here was lost to the floods. The current structure is a three span wooden footbridge built on concrete abutments and two stone piers that stand on the riverbed.

Broken Way Ford and Footbridge, St John's Chapel.

Ponderlane Footbridge

Ponderlane Footbridge stands near to the centre of St John's Chapel on the line of what was old Pinder Lane on the south side of the river. In older times the lane was called Punder Lonnen. The site is thought to have provided access via a ford to farms on the north side from the medieval period.

It is known that a new wooden bridge was built here in 1840, which needed re-railing and then re-beaming around 1869. In the severe flood of 9th March 1881, we are told, 'the south pier of the bridge was washed away just after some passengers had crossed over it. The end of the bridge on losing its support dropped a little and touched the water'.

The current bridge is a two span structure built on two steel beams and supported by concrete abutments and a centre pier. The handrails are of wood and a gate has been attached to the north side of the bridge to prevent animals from straying across it.

Pinder Lane was so called because a 'pinfold' existed nearby, which was a pound for the temporary enclosure of stray cattle or other animals. Drovers taking livestock long distances to market often made an overnight stop at the pinfold. Some animals had to be prepared for their journey. Geese often had the bottoms of their feet tarred and were then made to walk on sand to toughen up their soles for the long walk to the market at Tow Law.

Interestingly, the pinfold still exists here as the police house and garden. A 'pinder' was the person who looked after the pinfold.

Ponderlane Footbridge, St John's Chapel. On the line of old Pinder Lane.

Huntshield Stepping-Stones, Ford and Footbridge

Huntshield Stepping-Stones and Ford are said to be medieval and are thought to date to the 12th century. The potential for a river site to provide a safe fording point would have had a fundamental influence on the way that local medieval pathways and tracks developed. This is demonstrated by the fords of Huntshield, Ponderlane and Broken Way, where the lines of the ancient tracks that inter-connected them on both sides of the river are still visible today as minor roads and pathways in the area.

Huntshield Footbridge sits downstream of and adjacent to the ancient ford and is built on the abutments of an earlier structure, but the two piers at the centre of the bridge appear to be more modern. It is similar in design to a wooden footbridge further downriver, which was glued together from

Huntshield Stepping-Stones, Ford and Footbridge.

three prefabricated sections to create extra flexibility. The first bridge on this site is thought to date from the last half of the 19th century.

This site is somewhat unique to Weardale in that it is the only crossing to still provide the choice of three different modes of conveyance over the river.

A689 Road Bridge at Daddry Shield

The first bridge on this site was a single arched stone structure built in 1745. The village and bridge got their name from a gentleman called 'Doddry' who once lived in the area. The early bridge, however, was also known as 'Whites Brig or Bridge' after a man of that name who, in 'a fit of frenzy', threw himself off the top of it into the waters below.

Durham County Council replaced the stone structure with an iron bridge around 1890. The bridge was renewed yet again in the 1990s following flood damage. Half a mile downstream of Daddry Shield Bridge are the sites of a former bridge and cattle ford. The abutments of an old footbridge exist at

Windyside. They are constructed in the style of a dry stonewall and are thought to be of considerable antiquity. Timber decking is likely to have completed the structure and this location may provide an insight into the early techniques of bridge building that were developed in Weardale.

One hundred yards downstream of Windyside is the site of an old cattle ford that lies close to Westgate House.

Daddry Shield Bridge of the 1990s.

Whites Brig of 1745 at Daddry Shield. Here, in this late 19th century photograph, a three horse bus stands on the bridge.

The old dry stone abutments of Windyside Footbridge near Westgate.

Waterside House Ford, Footbridge and Stepping-Stones, Westgate

The humped-back wooden footbridge at Waterside House. Stepping-stones lie in the river below the bridge.

Two large timber posts on the south side of the river mark the former path of an old ford that once crossed the river at this place to emerge on the north bank close to the gable end of Waterside House. This river crossing once allowed the local farmer vehicle and animal access to his land on both sides of the river, but it now stands abandoned.

Adjacent to the old ford site is a humped-back wooden footbridge, which was erected around 1969. Its design is somewhat unique, in that it was constructed in three pre-fabricated sections and glued together on site to produce a bridge of improved flexibility, all without the use of nails! The bridge gives foot access from Windyside on the south side of the river to the village of Westgate. Immediately below the bridge are a set of stepping-stones, earlier versions of which are said to pre-date the ford. They will have been used for access to the village long before the erection of the footbridge.

Shallow Ford and Britton Bridge, Westgate

Shallow Ford is another of the medieval fords of Weardale and is said to date from the 13th century. Its name suggests that it has provided a safe, reliable crossing point over the centuries and it is still very much in use today. Access via the road on the south side of the river passes through the surviving abutments of an old rail bridge, which was erected around 1895.

Adjacent to the ford stands Britton Footbridge, which is named after Britton Hall on the north side of the river. An early photograph (below) shows the structure to be a wooden trestle bridge, with probably a single trestle at the river centre and natural stone abutments on each riverbank. A set of stepping-stones was in use here before the erection of a footbridge sometime after 1861. The attractive single span slightly arched steel bridge of today was erected around 2002 and made use of the substantial access paths and original stone abutments on site.

Shallow Ford and Britton Footbridge when it was a wooden trestle bridge. Note the spelling on this postcard of 'Brittain'. Courtesy of Frank Walton.

Shallow Ford and the Britton Footbridge of around 2002.

Haswicks Bridge, Westgate

A wooden bridge at Westgate was swept away by a flood on Christmas Day of 1824. In 1825 a new bridge was erected which was partly swept away in a flood of 1842. Following extensive repairs, it was swept away for a third time on 4th February 1852.

On 10th September 1852, the foundation stone was laid for a brand new stone bridge of two arches. During its construction it rained persistently for 16 weeks towards the end of 1852 and a pillar of the new bridge under construction was badly damaged. Having installed new pillar caps, it was decided to abandon construction work for that winter. The bridge was finally completed in October of 1853.

On 21st December 1853, a fatal accident occurred related to the construction of the bridge. One of the contractors, John Bainbridge, was taking stones on a horse and cart to level up the ends of the bridge. The horse slipped on the ice from a heavy frost of the previous night and crushed the poor chap against the wall. The unfortunate man died the next day of his injuries.

Despite the unfortunate history of the bridge, it stands today a most handsome structure. A railway arch was added to the bridge on the south side of the river around 1895.

Opposite page, top: Haswicks Bridge, Westgate, erected in 1853.

Opposite page, bottom: The railway arch on the south side of Haswicks Bridge added around 1895.

Brotherlee Footbridge

A map of 1861 shows this site to be a ford. It is reported that a wooden bridge at Brotherlee was swept off its piers by the severe flood of 9th March 1881, so the first footbridge on this site appears to have been erected sometime between 1861 and 1881.

In the flood of January 1995 the centre portion of the wooden footbridge was washed away and found itself deposited way downstream below the main bridge at Frosterley. The replacement beams between the first two piers from the north side of the river are of steel and not wood.

The bridge provides foot access for the community at Brotherlee (which now includes a caravan park) to the north bank of the Wear where there is a riverside footpath approximately one mile long to Westgate.

Around 300 yards downstream of the bridge, adjacent to where Park Burn joins the Wear, is the site of an old ford.

The footbridge at Brotherlee.

Cambokeels Mine Bridge

Around half a mile downstream of Brotherlee Footbridge, close to where the Westernhopeburn joins the Wear, is the site of an old industrial bridge associated with Cambokeels (also called Cammock Eels) lead, fluorspar and limestone mine. The history of the mine goes back to the middle of the 19th century when it was worked for lead by the Beaumont Company. Its output was poor however, and by 1871 the site had been abandoned.

In 1905 the mine was re-opened for fluorspar. Between 1915 and 1918 a self-acting incline was used to carry the ore down to the river via a rail track, which crossed the Wear over the bridge. Here, access was gained to sidings connected to the Wear Valley Line of 1895. The structure was a timber decked rail bridge standing on three stone piers. German POWs helped in the construction of the incline in September of 1915. Although the mine was worked intermittently throughout the 20th century, the bridge was demolished around 1968. In 1973 high quality fluorite was discovered and in the 1980s limestone was mined at much deeper levels within the mine. The site was eventually abandoned in 1989.

An aerial flight from the neighbouring Heights Quarry also crossed the river at this point. This quarry still operates today. A ford also existed here, which may have provided access to the quarry and mine for its workers living to the south of the river.

Eastgate Cement Works Conveyor Bridge

In 1964 a cement works was established on the north side of the Wear, just upstream of Eastgate at Blackies Ealand and Longley Pasture. At this time, a conveyor system was built to transfer powdered limestone from the quarry on the 'top site' down to the works at Eastgate for processing. The limestone/shale mix was delivered at a rate of 180 tons per hour, and crossed the river to the works via a conveyor bridge erected at Paddock Nook.

The cement was transported by rail between 1964 and 1993 and thereafter by road to Teesside, Tyneside and Scotland. In August 2002, owners Lafarge closed the plant with the loss of 150 jobs.

Many schemes have been considered for the creation of new jobs at the former cement works site. In September 2004, a project was undertaken to drill 3,000 feet into the earth to search for 'hot rocks'. Hot water associated with the heat source could then be used to create an energy efficient theme and business park. A successful conclusion to the project was announced in December of that year and demolition of the old cement works site was planned to start at the beginning of 2005.

The Cement Works Conveyor Bridge at Eastgate, erected around 1964.

Eastgate Rail Bridge

On 21st October 1895, the final extension of the Wear Valley Line was opened and the scheme included the erection of a rail bridge at Eastgate around this time. It crosses the river at a position adjacent to the now abandoned cement works. The structure is a two span, riveted trough deck iron bridge on natural stone abutments and centre pier. Today unfortunately it looks sadly neglected.

The last freight service crossed the bridge in 1968 and what is left of the 1895 line extension terminates just west of here.

The villages of Eastgate and Westgate are so called because they stand at the former eastern and western entrances to the large hunting park that belonged in medieval times to the Prince Bishops of Durham.

Eastgate Rail Bridge of 1895, with the cement works in the background.

Hag Bridge, Eastgate

A ford was the only means available to cross the river here in earlier times. By 1861 however, 'Hagford Bridge' a wooden structure for horses and foot passengers was present on this site, but it was damaged in the severe flood of March 1881.

This suggests that the stone structure of two arches was not erected until after 1881. The flood of January 1995 damaged the stone bridge to the extent that it was demolished five months later. The replacement bridge of 1996 was designed and built by Durham County Council using a steel deck supplied by Mabey and Johnson. The structure is set on natural stone abutments and has a span of 29.5 metres.

The flood-damaged Hag Bridge at Eastgate, demolished in June 1995. Courtesy of Peter Bowes.

The modern Hag Bridge, erected by Durham County Council in 1996.

Stanhope West Rail Bridge

Stanhope West Rail Bridge was erected around 1895 when the final extension of the railway was completed to Wearhead and is sited one mile to the west of the town. The riveted iron trough deck rail bridge rests on natural stone abutments and two river piers. It proved impossible to extend this new line west from the original railway terminus at Stanhope, so a brand new station was erected.

The town of Stanhope is often referred to as the capital of Weardale. Its name derives from two old English words, 'stan' meaning stone and 'hop' denoting side valley, so Stanhope stands for 'stone side valley'. The name originally applied to the valley associated with the Stanhope Burn that joins the River Wear here, but it was eventually adopted by the ancient settlement that developed nearby. In medieval times, the Bishop of Durham used the Park of Stanhope for hunting pursuits.

Stanhope West Rail Bridge, erected around 1895.

The Stone Bridge, Stanhope

The handsome 'Stone Bridge' straddles the Wear at a point where the river surges through a narrow gorge of green basaltic rock or 'whin' creating a vista that is surely one of the gems of Weardale. The observer really needs to be at river level to experience the special atmosphere that nature and bridge builder have created between them. The bridge is often called 'Briggen Winch' as is the stretch of river just downstream of the structure.

A narrow bridge of one arch and suitable for packhorses was erected here sometime before 1400. Underneath its arch were three chamfered ribs said to be of the same form as those displayed in Stanhope Church. The bridge was widened in 1792 when a second arch without ribs was added directly downstream of the old one. Two distinct building styles are therefore visible beneath the combined arch of the present bridge, which is almost semicircular in shape and has a span of 36 feet. New parapets were erected in 1837 and further repairs are thought to have been carried out some 40 years later, as the date of AD 1876 is carved into the western parapet.

In 1919 a German field cannon found itself unceremoniously

Stone Bridge or Briggen Winch, Stanhope.

dumped in the river at Briggen Winch. The captured gun had been erected at West End, but local war veterans took exception to it, towed it away and dumped it into the river beside the bridge. A large angry crowd secured their release from the police station where they had been locked away for their actions. It is said that Briggen Winch is built on the site of a former Roman structure. It is also the site of probably the earliest post-Roman bridge in the Wear Valley, for an ancient structure of wood and/or animal hides is thought to have existed here.

Stanhope Stepping-Stones and Ford

Stanhope Ford is thought to be Roman in date and lies on the line of an ancient Roman road over Egglestone Moor. The age of the stepping-stones are unknown, but the present concrete blocks are not original to the site.

The ford now lies on the B6278 road connecting Egglestone to Consett. The nearby park and open-air swimming pool attract many visitors to the site in the summer and Stanhope Ford has become something of a 'novelty attraction' to some motorists, who often compete with each other to see who can raise the highest wall of water and soak the users of the stepping-stones. This is often considered to be harmless fun but locally the ford is treated with more caution. Approach signs not to use the ford in conditions of flood and depth gauges are ignored at the driver's peril. In 2004, a rescue helicopter saved the drivers of two vehicles stuck on the crossing. One car had attempted to cross the ford when water was running at a depth of almost $1/2$ metre. Investigations into the use of barriers or light protection systems are taking place, but there is a possibility that the ford could close altogether with traffic being diverted to the nearby Stone Bridge.

The Stepping-Stones and Ford at Stanhope. Another pedestrian gets a soaking!

Stanhope Footbridge

The early footbridge on this site was called Unthank Bridge, after the nearby hall and mill of that name. The wooden bridge is shown on a map of 1861, but the year of its construction is not known. The structure seems to have miraculously escaped the serious damage that the flood of 1881 wreaked on much of the surrounding area.

In 1902 a fine wooden suspension bridge was erected on the site, which was given the name of Coronation Bridge to commemorate the crowning of Edward VII in that year. The people of Stanhope were destined to enjoy this splendid structure for less than 50 years, for in the spring of 1947 it was washed away in a flood.

Shortly after the loss of Coronation Bridge, the Royal Engineers erected a replacement footbridge. This existing bridge is a metal structure, which rests on the original natural stone abutments.

Above: The Stanhope Footbridge of 1902.

Left: The current Stanhope Footbridge, erected around 1948.

Stanhope Central Rail Bridge

Stanhope Central Rail Bridge was the first bridge to the west of the newly erected Stanhope Station on the line extension to Wearhead that opened in 1895. Looking downriver from The Butts provides an excellent vantage point to admire this late Victorian structure which still stands proudly over the Wear. It is similar in size and construction to Stanhope West Rail Bridge one mile upstream and rests on two natural stone central river piers and abutments. Until closure of the line on 29th June 1953, four passenger trains a day had crossed this bridge, although freight services did continue to function until 1968.

Stanhope Central Rail Bridge of 1894/5, as viewed from The Butts.

Stanhope East Rail Bridge

The Frosterley and Stanhope Railway Company extended the Wear Valley Line to Stanhope in 1862, primarily to gain access to the numerous quarries of the area. Stanhope East Rail Bridge was erected at this time close to Shittlehope Burn Farm, but was to survive for only 19 years before the flood of 9th March 1881 took its frightful toll on the town.

An eyewitness account is summarised as follows. At the railway station water levels rose by the hour and the railway plates were said to be the only part of the track visible above water between bridge and station. The river came into contact with the bridge around 8 o'clock and a crowd had gathered to watch in trepidation as the rising river water bombarded the centre pier of the bridge. The last train had crossed the bridge at 5.10 but prudently; all trains thereafter had been cancelled. At 8 o'clock the south pier of the bridge was dramatically washed away by a torrent of water and the southern half of the bridge was engulfed in the ensuing deluge.

A water main and Stanhope Gas Company's gas main both crossed the river on this bridge and both were fractured when the structure was washed away. Lights flickered momentarily then the town was suddenly plunged into darkness as word quickly spread that Stanhope had lost its rail bridge.

The date of the replacement two span iron bridge standing here is not known, but a temporary bridge was quickly erected to restore the rail service into Stanhope.

Above: Stanhope East Rail Bridge.

Left: The laying of new sleepers at Stanhope East Rail Bridge for the re-opening of the Stanhope to Wolsingham section of the line in 2004.

The Gas Works Bridge

At the place where Shittlehope Burn flows into the Wear on the site of an old ford, an iron road bridge with two side piers and a centre pier of stone was erected in 1862 for the use of 'horse and cart traffic'. The name Shittlehope is said to derive from an old English word 'Scyttel' meaning steep sided.

Like its upstream neighbour this bridge was another victim of the 1881 flood. Two hours after the upstream rail bridge was swept away, a crowd watched the effect of the swollen river on the road bridge. The rain had stopped and the moon broke through the clouds to cast an eerie light over the surging swollen river. The south pier of the bridge fell and that side of the iron structure went with it, leaving the other half of the bridge still resting on its pier. The northern half of the bridge then fell into the river and was washed away. 'The ruins of this bridge were such as to render the scene picturesque, if deplorable and showed in the wreck a good example of the effects of the incalculable power of this extraordinary flood' wrote eyewitness and local author William Morley Egglestone.

By 1868 a gas works was operating on the south side of the river between Railway Terrace and the bridge, and the structure was consequently known as the 'The Gas Works Bridge'. A replacement wooden trestle bridge was erected sometime after the loss of the iron structure. Interestingly, the wooden trestle bridge and gas works are the subject of a remarkable watercolour painted by a German Prisoner of War who was captive at Shittlehope Camp around 1918.

In 1958 the wooden trestle bridge was replaced by a two span concrete structure on red brick abutments and centre pier. This bridge still stands today, but the Victorian buildings of the gas works were demolished between 1961

The German POW watercolour of the wooden trestle bridge at Shittlehope Burn, painted around 1918. Courtesy of Ann Wilkinson.

and 1970. Stumps of the old wooden trestle bridge, however, still stand in the shadow of its successor near the north bank of the river.

Around half a mile downriver of the bridge is the site of an old ford near Low Bat.

The 'Gas Works Bridge' of 1958 at Shittlehope Burn.

Rogerley Rail Bridge

This Victorian rail bridge stands near East Burry Holme around one mile downstream of Shittlehope Burn Bridge, on a bend in the river midway between Rogerley Lodge and Rogerley Hall. It dates to around 1862 and is a trough deck iron rail bridge standing on stone abutments and centre pier. Unlike its two neighbours upstream, it survived the 1881 flood.

Rogerley is famous for Frosterley Marble that was mined at its quarry as long as 700 years ago. The material is not really marble, but a black limestone containing quantities of white fossilised horn coral dating to the carboniferous period. Columns of Frosterley Marble were installed inside Durham Cathedral around 1350.

Rogerley Quarry still operates today on a commercial basis in an abandoned 19th century mine and produces mineral specimens for collectors. When the mines themselves were active, workers avidly collected fluorescent specimens of crystal from the veins of ore, which they called 'bonny bits'. Some miners in their leisure time made spar boxes, the word 'spar' being derived from the word fluorspar. The specimens were attached to the walls of glass-fronted cases or sometimes pressed into sculptured shapes of plaster of Paris and displayed under glass domes. The spar boxes recreated the crystal grottoes of the 18th century or street scenes of the 19th century, but examples of pyramids, trees and rotundas exist. Exhibitions and competitions have been held in St John's Chapel since the 1880s. A permanent collection of spar boxes is displayed at Killhope Lead Mining Museum. The largest example known is the Egglestone Spar Box made by Joseph Egglestone of Huntshieldford in the early 20th century.

Rogerley Rail Bridge near East Burry Holme, erected around 1862.

Frosterley Bridge

The ancient village name of Frosterley is said to derive from 'the foresters clearing'. Its bridge stands just to the west of the town's railway station. An old stone bridge here was washed away in the great flood of November 1771. It was replaced by a temporary wooden structure until County Surveyor Ignatius Bonomi designed the present stone bridge of three arches, which was erected in 1814. In 1862 the roadway at the north end of the bridge was raised at Mellbutts Bank to allow the rail extension to Stanhope to pass beneath it.

The bridge was restored and widened in 1995/96 and was re-opened on 11th March 1996 by Councillor Don Ross, Chairman of Durham County Council Environment Committee, assisted by local schoolchildren from Frosterley Primary School. The Engineer was D.J. Newbegin and the contractor was John Mowlem Construction plc.

For several days after the severe flood of 1881, Frosterley Station was the terminus of the Wear Valley Line until repairs to the rail bridge at Stanhope were made.

The Fly Bridge, Frosterly

Around 500 yards downstream of Bonomi's Bridge at Frosterley stand the abutments of an old quarry structure called the Fly Bridge. The bridge was erected over the River Wear in the 1870s to connect the extended limestone quarry at Bishopley to a siding in the station yard at Frosterley.

The Frosterley and Bishopley areas were known to be rich in limestone and extensive quarries were established on both sides of the Wear Valley to serve the blast furnaces of Teesside. Transport of the limestone had been made

possible by the opening of a rail service between Witton Junction and Frosterley-Bishopley in August of 1847.

At the peak of production there were 13 miles of quarries in Frosterley and Stanhope. By the end of the 1920s however, quarrying had sharply declined and the Fly Bridge at Frosterley was one of its casualties.

The surviving abutments of the Fly Bridge at Frosterley, erected in the 1870s.

Kenneth's Bridge, Frosterley

It is said that floods have washed Kenneth's Footbridge away four times in the last thirty years. The site has not always enjoyed the services of a bridge however, as crossing the river here meant the use of the ford or stepping-stones in earlier times.

The structure is named after local joiner and cabinetmaker Kenneth Maddison who built a footbridge here in 1936/37 with timber from Burnhope Reservoir. Curiously, Kenneth's Bridge never quite made it to the south bank of the river so a certain degree of athleticism must have been required to use it!

Nevertheless it replaced a small suspension bridge just downstream, which had been in use by the Pease quarrymen for some years. It is thought that funds for the suspension bridge were raised by subscription.

In the flood of January 1995, a caravan was washed away from its standage at a site upriver. On approaching Kenneth's Bridge the caravan narrowly failed to perform a complete somersault over the bridge and its handrails were damaged.

Kenneth's Bridge, Frosterley. Washed away four times in floods.

Broadwood Rail Bridge

A rail line from Witton Junction to Frosterley was opened on 3rd August 1847 and Broadwood Rail Bridge was erected around this time. On a map of 1861 the bridge is shown to be a wooden structure, but the present bridge is of iron and built on abutments and piers of natural stone. The width and appearance of the two river piers suggests that they were erected to accommodate a double track.

Broadwood Iron Rail Bridge, erected sometime after 1861.

Broadwood Ford and Road Bridge

A few yards downstream of the rail bridge stand Broadwood Ford and then Broadwood Road Bridge. They both provide access to the Durham Industrial Minerals Plant formerly Broadwood Quarry, as well as to local farms. A road bridge was present on this site by the mid 19th century. The present road bridge stands on concrete abutments and two river piers and was built in the 1970s to replace a narrow structure immediately west of Broadwood Lodge. The Broadwood area is so called because its lands were anciently possessed by a family of that name.

Broadwood Quarry was one of Frosterley's major 19th century limestone mines. Lime burning for the Broadwood Estate and tar making were also developed here but more recently the processing of fluorspar has kept the site active. Broadwood Mill site was abandoned in 1901. It is said that Frosterley Marble was mined in this area over 900 years ago.

Around three quarters of a mile downstream of the Broadwood Bridges is the site of an old ford at Greenbank.

Broadwood Ford and the Road Bridge of the 1970s.

New Bridge, Holebeck Mill

A map of 1861 shows this site to be served by a ford. At some point after this a wooden bridge is said to have been erected, possibly to provide access for local farmers to Holebeck Mill where their corn was milled. Within living memory its replacement structure has always been known as 'The New Bridge'. It was updated in the early 1990s and a modern four span concrete and steel structure on three stone piers now provides a crossing point not only to Holebeck House, Sunniside, and Coves House Farm, but also to the Kingfisher Country Caravan Park. A track on the east side of the river connects the bridges of Holebeck and Broadwood via East and West Biggins.

Half a mile downstream from Holebeck Bridge lies the site of an old ford at Windy Nook.

The New Bridge at Holebeck Mill, updated in the 1990s.

Wolsingham Bridge

The present Wolsingham Road Bridge also known as 'Wear's Bridge' is of lattice girder construction and was built by Durham County Council in 1894. It replaced a stone bridge of two arches built in 1772, which in turn replaced an older structure swept away in the great flood of 1771.

It is said that ancient piles exist under the current iron bridge. Some sort of structure crossed the river at this site as early as the 15th century, as indulgences for a period of forty days were granted in October of 1479 to those who helped in its erection. By the reign of Elizabeth I, however, it is said that this bridge was in a state of decay. In 1722 a bridge here was washed away in what became known as 'Slater's Flood'. Slater was a bailiff of Durham, who having died in that year was unable to be buried because of the floodwaters. When this structure was lost it was thought necessary to build a temporary footbridge 'until a bridge of stone for carts and carriages may be built'.

The Wolsingham Bridge of 1772.

Wolsingham Rail Bridge

The rail bridge sits around half a mile to the south east of Wolsingham close to the site of the Weardale Steel Company. It once carried the Bishop Auckland and Weardale Railway to Wolsingham Station sited on the south side of the river a short distance from the town. It is a substantial iron structure sitting on wide natural stone built piers and was erected around 1847. The piers of the bridge were designed to accommodate a double track if ever required. The line itself officially opened on 3rd August 1847.

The nearby steel works were established in 1864 prior to their purchase in 1885 by J. Rogerson and Company. At its peak the factory employed 500 men and made all manner of forgings and castings. They were contractors to HM Naval and War Departments and manufactured steering gear for HM battleship *Neptune* and a 6 ton cast steel anchor head for the RMS *Mauretania*. In 1930 the works were taken over by the Marr and Thompson families and operated as the Wolsingham Steel Company, when a long association with the Sunderland shipbuilding industry developed. When the Sunderland shipyards closed, the factory successfully sought alternative markets abroad and the site now operates as Weardale Steel Ltd.

Wolsingham Rail Bridge, constructed around 1847.

Low Wiserley Sawmill Bridge

An Ordnance Survey map of the 1920s reveals the existence of what may have been a bridge situated approximately one mile downstream from Wolsingham Rail Bridge, and around a quarter of a mile to the east of Low Wiserley. Timber from a sawmill located in the Wiserley Plantation area was transported to the river via a one and a half mile stretch of tramway, before crossing the river at this point to link into the main Wear Valley Railway. This structure seems to have had a brief lifespan, for it is not shown to exist on an Ordnance Survey map of 1934.

Around 500 yards further downstream is the site of an old ford between a track from Bradley Cottage on the south side of the river and Scotch Isle Farm via Crook Lane on the north side.

Black Bank Plantation Footbridge

This bridge is the first of two former structures that were erected along a stretch of river skirting Black Bank Plantation. The footbridge was sited close to where Bradley Beck flows into the Wear. Bradley Mill once stood on the north side of the river, which may provide an explanation for the siting of a footbridge here. No bridge was here before 1861, but it is shown on maps of 1932 and 1964. Today a stone abutment survives on the north bank and concrete foundations lie discarded at the river centre. There are indications on site that steel beams were used to strengthen the structure in its later life.

Brown's Bridge

A rail bridge once crossed the river to the east side of Black Bank Plantation close to where Eels Beck joins the Wear. Its flat timber deck rested on five substantial pairs of crossed braced wooden piles set in concrete foundations equally spaced across the river. The bridge carried plantation timber to the nearby main rail line and was known as Brown's Bridge after the family that ran the business. It is likely to have been erected around 1892 when the company was provided with railway sidings and nearby Harperley Station was enlarged. Extensive concrete foundations remain on site and two pairs of timber piles still stand at each river bank.

Half a mile downstream lies the site of Low Harperley Ford. The ford was used for the movement of cattle across the river, but a resident from several years ago tells me that farm tractors often used the ford, for example to bring groceries across the river from the weekly delivery van.

Harperley Footbridge

The present footbridge at Low Harperley is a quite unique structure for it appears to be the only all-aluminium bridge over the Wear. It bears a nameplate informing us that it was built in January 1990 by Linkleters Ltd of North Shields, who were 'specialists in the design and manufacture of marine gangways for both ship and shore installations'. Its nominal dimensions are stated as being 45.6 metres x 0.750 metres and its max load is 17,435 kg, which translates into persons as being 232. Whether 232 people could get on to the bridge at the same time however is open to debate!

The bridge lies close to the site of the old Harperley Railway Station on the Wear Valley Branch Railway, which was built in 1847, originally as a private station for the use of the owners of nearby Harperley Hall. The station was once said to be haunted.

The first footbridge here was erected sometime before 1861. A 20th century wooden bridge was swept away in floods and was replaced for a while by a wooden plank! A steel footbridge was then erected, which is known to have been in place in 1974. The aluminium footbridge, which dates from 1990, is thought to have been the replacement for its steel predecessor.

Harperley Bridge united the communities from both sides of the river not only for farm access, social gatherings and school travel, but also for worship, for a small wooden chapel once sat close to the site of the bridge. A quiet rural atmosphere now embraces Low Harperley, but by 1892, an overhead flight from Knitsley Quarry crossed the river to sidings close to the station where its cargo of ganister clay was transported away by the rail system. The bridge now stands in splendid isolation but can be used by walkers of the Weardale Way.

A map of 1861 shows a ford just 100 yards downstream of the bridge.

Unlike the wooden footbridge of the mid 20th century, the nearby Harperley POW Camp has survived to modern times and is now open to the public. It is the most complete example of a purpose-built POW Camp left in the country and is a scheduled ancient monument. The camp was erected in 1943 to hold low security risk prisoners from Italy and

The present Harperley Footbridge, erected in 1990.

Germany. At its peak, around 900 men were held there. By 1947 the majority of men had been repatriated home but a handful were granted permission to stay in England, three of whom live to this day in anonymity around Wearside.

Further downstream from Harperley Bridge, over a two and a half mile stretch of river to Witton-le-Wear, lie the sites of three equally spaced fords. The first was around the Low Shipley area. The workers at Witton Quarry perhaps used McNeil Ford near Ciscorn Bank. Finally, Garth Ford was sited near Witton Bottoms.

Witton Road Bridge on the A68

This modern road bridge was erected in 1969 some 250 yards upstream of the old stone arched structure, when Witton-le-Wear was given its bypass as part of the upgrading of the A68. It was designed by Mott, Hay and Anderson and built by Durham County Council Direct Labour Organisation. It has reinforced concrete beams and deck set on reinforced concrete piers. The spans of the bridge are 15.24 metres, 24.38 metres, 33.52 metres and 23.62 metres.

Before its construction traffic had passed through Witton-le-Wear via High Street then travelled down Clemmy Bank to cross the Wear over the old bridge. It then rejoined the line of the modern A68 near Fitches Grange.

The bypass was welcome not only for reducing traffic flow through the village, but also for the protection it afforded to the old stone bridge.

Witton Road Bridge on the A68, constructed in 1969.

Witton Bridge

It is recorded that on 6th October 1313 an indulgence of 40 days was granted to those who contributed to the fabric of the bridge at Witton in Weardale. A bridge is therefore thought to have been present on this site since this date.

On 12th March 1764 the northern arch of Witton Bridge collapsed. On 17th November 1771 the bridge here was destroyed in the great flood of that year. It was rebuilt but was swept away yet again on 10th October 1787. The build date of the present bridge is not known, but it is likely to be from a period just after the 1787 loss. It is an ashlar sandstone humped-back bridge with two segmental arches of total span 150 feet. The bridge has no footpath but the stone parapets contain pedestrian refuges.

Less than half a mile downstream of Witton Bridge towards the area of Lively Bank Plantation is the site of an old ford and footbridge. Both these crossings were here before 1861 and may have provided access to Witton Railway Station on the north side of the river. The footbridge has not survived within the living memory of residents. A further half-mile downstream, around the area of Holme Wood, is another old ford site.

Witton Bridge, erected around 1788.

Witton Park Viaduct, Footbridge and Road Bridge

November of 1843 saw the opening of a rail line from Shildon Junction to Crook, which passed through Witton Park to cross the River Wear by way of a rail viaduct of timber construction. By 3rd August 1847, the line had been extended to Frosterley from Witton Junction on the north side of the river. The new communication network resulted in the opening in 1846 of an ironworks to the south east of the viaduct on Paradise Fields. A replacement viaduct of natural stone was then erected in 1854. Red bricks were incorporated into its construction to enhance the inner parts of its arches and provide greater strength. In the absence of a road system virtually all the raw materials, food and domestic goods that Witton Park required at this time were delivered by rail.

In the early 1900s a narrow single carriageway steel road bridge was added to the stone viaduct at a lower level and adjacent to an existing footbridge. New stone abutments were attached to the two pillars of a centre arch to carry the structure over the river, one on the upstream side of one pillar and one on the downstream side of the second support. The road bridge therefore approaches the viaduct at an angle and actually passes through the viaduct arch at the centre of the river.

For the first time this bridge, which opened on 23rd August 1904, gave direct road communication to Witton Park from Witton-le-Wear and Crook and the highway was called 'The New Road'. The narrow road bridge survives today in its original form but the footbridge was removed some years ago.

The ironworks closed in 1884 causing great distress to the community and the site became an eyesore. In 2003, however, Paradise Fields were finally restored to their former glory and were opened in June of that year by conservationist David Bellamy.

Just downstream of the viaduct is the site of an industrial ford, which was developed in the 1950s for access to the sand and gravel beds on both sides of the river.

Witton Park Viaduct of 1854 and the Road Bridge erected in 1904.

The stone viaduct and footbridge at Witton Park before the building of the road bridge.

The ford at Witton Park, developed in the 1950s for access to sand and gravel beds.

Craggs Suspension Bridge at Escombe

Bishop Auckland is famous for its medieval bridge and Victorian viaduct, but for a period of over 50 years another remarkable bridge existed nearby. Miners living at Escombe and working at the Toronto Colliery faced a two-mile walk to work along a meandering riverside footpath, before crossing the Wear at Bishop Skirlaws Bridge to make their way to the pit at the top of Newton Cap.

A blacksmith at Toronto Colliery called Robert Craggs came to the rescue. Around 1895, he designed and built a bridge at Escombe just downstream of Dunelme Chare. It was a footbridge suspended on two pit cage haulage cables. The bridge was in constant use by the miners but following the General Strike of 1926, the pit was slow to re-open and by 1937 the bridge has fallen into disrepair. It is thought to have been dismantled during the Second World War. The bridge foundations at Escombe were washed away in a flood of 1988, but it is said that some evidence of the structure still exists on the opposite side of the river.

Before the construction of this bridge it was possible to cross the river half a mile further downstream near Broken Bank where a 19th century ford existed.

Craggs Suspension Bridge at Escombe, built around 1895.

The village of Escombe is better known for its Saxon church, said to have been erected in 675. Irish influences in its shape and design, however, suggest an even earlier construction date. It was built at least in part with stones removed from the Roman fort at Binchester two miles away and the River Wear is thought to have been used to transport the blocks to Escombe. Some stones used in the building of the church have Roman inscriptions on them, which were set into the walls 'upside down'. This may have been a display of rejection of the previous Roman culture by the Anglo-Saxon builders, or an attempt to banish any evil influences that they believed lingered in buildings of the past.

Newton Cap or Bishop Skirlaw's Bridge

Bishop Auckland's rapid growth as a colliery town occurred throughout the 19th century, but its name is associated with a much earlier time in history when Auckland Castle became the official residence of the Bishop of Durham some 800 years ago. Its medieval two-arched bridge at Newton Cap was built in 1388 by Bishop Skirlaw on the site of an older bridge thought to be Roman in origin. The central pier of the 1388 bridge is said to actually encapsulate the remains of the original pier of the Roman structure. The northern segmental arch has a span of 101 feet, whilst the more pointed southern arch spans 91 feet. The bridge once had a gateway at its southern end. By 1565 the structure was described as being in great decay.

An inscription on the western parapet of the bridge commemorates 'Edwd Palfrey's Leep of 1774'. Palfrey was a prizefighter but was equally renowned for fighting dogs and bulls. In a drunken state and followed by a large crowd, he crossed the bridge on his way to fight a bull. The contest was cancelled so he returned to the bridge followed by the throng. Historian Fordyce tells us that to appease the crowd he decided 'to show them a few antics upon the battlement of the bridge'. He fell off, but being unhurt climbed back onto the bridge where he challenged all-comers to jump after him. It is said that he leapt three

Commemorative stone for Edwd Palfrey's Leep of 1744 from Newton Cap Bridge.

times but on the third occasion he 'dashed his brains out'.

Around 1900 two cantilever footpaths were installed on girders leaving the original parapets intact. In 2002 the cantilevers were removed and replaced by a single footpath.

The conversion of nearby Newton Cap Viaduct into a road bridge in 1995 has done much to protect Bishop Skirlaw's ancient bridge from the excesses of modern day traffic, although high-sided vehicles are sometimes diverted on to it from the viaduct when strong winds prevail.

Archaeologists tell us that the course of Dere Street ran from Fylands Bridge on the River Gaunless to loop around Bishop Auckland on its way to the Fort at Binchester before crossing the Wear nearby. Since 1872 however, debate has often centred round a counter postulation that Dere Street ran more directly from Fylands Bridge in almost a straight line through Bishop Auckland to the Roman bridge at Newton Cap. Evidence of a nearby large Roman settlement, perhaps a fort, also exists here. This counter premise is considered somewhat controversial, for if the fort at Binchester was not actually on Dere Street it cannot be accorded the title of 'Vinovia'.

Bishop Skirlaw's Bridge of 1388. The centre pier is said to encapsulate part of a former Roman structure.

Newton Cap Viaduct

The construction of the Newton Cap Rail Viaduct began in 1854 but the bridge was not opened until 1st April 1857. Problems encountered in the building of the foundations meant that they had to be sunk 20 feet below the riverbed. This magnificent viaduct containing eleven arches each of 60 feet span and 100 feet height served Bishop Auckland as a rail bridge for 111 years, until its closure in 1968.

The work to convert the viaduct into a road bridge started in September 1993. It was widened by 13 feet to accommodate a new two-way road system incorporating a footpath on each side. The builders used reinforced concrete saddle-deck slabs featuring pre-cast concrete parapets to lie on top of the stone viaduct deck and provide a new road surface, which at the same time created a weather-sealed roof over the old structure.

The Right Hon Derek Foster MP opened the 'Newton Cap and Toronto Bypass' on 21st July 1995. The Engineer was D.J. Newbegin, Director of Environment, Durham County Council. The Environment Department, Durham County Council and Bullen Consultants created the design. The contractor was John Mowlem Construction plc. The viaduct conversion is thought to be the first of its kind in England and was carried out at a total cost of £4.25 million. During the conversion, 4,310 cubic metres of concrete and 758 tonnes of steel were utilised.

Because the viaduct stands in such an exposed position, modern communication has enabled a wind anemometer and weather vane fitted on the bridge to relay details of prevailing conditions to the local weather centre.

The plaque on the viaduct commemorating the 'rail to road' conversion bears the inscription 'Viaducts will endure for ages'.

In his book of 1872, *The History and Characteristics of Bishop Auckland,* author Matthew Richley states 'In more modern times, races were held upon The Flatts opposite the lower end of Wear Chare; and on those occasions a temporary wooden bridge was thrown across the River Wear, and a toll of one penny exacted for passing over it.' This temporary structure was located some 500 yards downstream of the site of the viaduct.

Less than two miles downstream of the viaduct lies

Newton Cap Viaduct of 1854, converted to a road bridge in the early 1990s.

Newton Cap Viaduct crossing the river.

the site of what is thought to be a Roman bridge. It is said that a bridge of 'stone and timber' existed at the point where the Roman road of Dere Street crossed the River Wear. The Roman fort at Binchester, which is considered to be 'Vinovia', is thought to have been erected in the 1st and 2nd centuries to protect this bridge. Recent debate however, has promoted the site of nearby Bishop Skirlaw's Bridge as being an alternative location for the Roman bridge associated with Dere Street.

The Colliery Bridges at Newfield

Two 19th century bridges and a structure from the turn of the 20th century may have existed in a 300 yard stretch of riverside adjacent to the neighbouring sites of the Newfield and John George Collieries.

The first bridge, possibly of simple timber construction, is thought to have served a mid 19th century tramway taking coal and possibly coke north across the river to the Newfield Colliery disposal point. Its existence is suggested at this place on a map of 1861 close to a mineshaft on the south bank of the river at Half Moon Plantation, but the bridge is shown to be no longer present on maps of 1934.

The second structure was erected a short distance downstream as the main rail bridge for the two collieries and was close to the houses of Bridge Row in an area known as The Challies. The chief role of this bridge was to take Newfield coals and coke south over the river to the main NER line at nearby Hunwick Station. This bridge was a more significant structure than its two neighbours and, although again of timber construction, was built on substantial natural stone abutments, probably in the 1840s. The presence of this bridge is confirmed on Ordnance Survey maps of 1857 and 1934.

The third bridge is not thought to have been erected until the early 20th century. It is again likely to have been a simple wooden structure, perhaps a trestle bridge built to take a mineral tramway over the river and carry coals and coke north to the Newfield Colliery disposal point. Its existence is confirmed on Ordnance Survey maps of 1907, 1920, 1934 and 1939. The stumps of the bridge are said to have survived and can still be seen in the riverbed today.

A complex network of associated mineral lines also connected these bridges to the Todd Hill Incline and its wagonway bridge half a mile further downstream at the site now occupied by the Pay Bridge.

Newfield Colliery was closed around 1960 and its main rail bridge dismantled except for its abutments around 1965. The colliery re-opened on a small scale around 1979 and the site still maintains its link with coal today, where a coking plant operates as the Newfield Works of Eldon Colliery. Raw materials are now imported and in the absence of its bridges, its freight is transported by road.

A surviving abutment of the main Newfield Colliery Rail Bridge.

The Pay Bridge

The first structure on this site was a mineral line rail bridge of wooden fabrication that was erected in 1838 to accommodate the new West Durham Railway Line. The bridge was designed by J. and B. Green and built by J. Welsh and Son for a total cost of £3,856. It was 206 feet in length and was composed of two laminated arches each of 79 feet span, resting on natural stone abutments and a central river pier. Its 43 feet wide platform, which had four lines of rails across it, sloped to the south east at an incline of 1 in 28. Access was available within the bridge to a farm on the west bank of the river.

The following was reported in the *Durham Chronicle* of 1st June 1838 under the headline 'Narrow Escape'. 'During the heavy flood of Tuesday night whilst the workmen were employed on cranes at the bridge erecting for the West Durham Railway Company near Byers Green, the scaffolding was overmined by the rising flood and a number of men immersed in the water. Six of the men were carried downriver upon single planks for a distance of three quarters of a mile but fortunately all were rescued without injury.'

The West Durham Railway Line was built to connect into the Clarence Railway of 1837 at Byers Green. The new line ran west from Byers Green down to the River Wear via the Todd Hill Incline. Here it crossed the wooden bridge to pass the sidings of Willington Colliery before continuing up to Helmington Row by way of the Sunny Brow Incline to access the collieries of Bowdon Close and High Jobs Hill. By 1841 the line had been extended to Billy Row where it terminated at the Old White Lea Colliery. It is thought that the mineral line and hence the bridge were abandoned around the end of the 19th century.

After the abandonment of the rail bridge a footbridge was constructed adjacent to the old structure, possibly making use of the original abutments. Its riveted iron construction suggests that it was erected late 19th/early 20th century. It is said that the Pay Bridge was so called because miners working in collieries to the east of the bridge needed to travel across it to receive their pay. The name is most likely to have been derived however, from the fact that it operated in its early days as a toll bridge. In the 1970s the bridge suffered flood damage, evidence of which can still be seen today on the surviving central pier.

Around 300 yards downstream of the Pay Bridge, close to where old Willington Colliery was situated, is the site of a yet another mid 19th century mineral line rail bridge. The mineral line ran down the Oakenshaw Incline from its colliery of 1855 to pass Brancepeth Colliery and cross the main NER line near Willington Station. From here the line passed Bank Head to cross the river via the bridge and connect into the abovementioned West Durham Rail Line.

The flood damaged central pier of the Pay Bridge.

Jubilee Bridge

In 1887 a three span trough deck iron road bridge was erected on natural stone abutments to the south east of Willington, 'chiefly through the exertions of Reverend Dr Hoopell'. Unusually, the deck rested on two pairs of tubular cross-braced iron piers, which were set into concrete on the riverbed. The bridge crossed the river about a mile and a quarter north west of Byers Green taking the place of a dangerous ford on the site. It opened up communications with Willington and Durham and also to the west and north of the county. The foundation stone was laid on 21st June 1887 by Ralph Peverell Esq. The bridge was constructed by the Auckland District Highway Board assisted by voluntary contributions. Ashmore, Benson, Pease and Co of Stockton-on-Tees were the contractors, under the direction of Engineer J. Heslop. It was called the Queen Victoria Jubilee Bridge because of the Queen's Golden Jubilee celebrations of that year. One buttress of the old bridge still remains on the south side of the river.

In 1990 Durham County Council erected a new reinforced concrete bridge just upstream of the old 1887 structure. The engineer was D.J. Newbegin, Director of the Environment. The Minister for Road and Traffic, Christopher Chope OBE MP, opened the bridge on 18th October 1990.

Some 200 yards downstream of Jubilee Bridge near The Batts lies the site of an old ford. Further downstream at Byers Green is the site of an old ford and ferry at the place where Wear Road approaches the river. The ferry operated just upstream of the ford. No signs of its existence are now visible, but it is shown on 1861 and 1932 maps. On an area of river close to the ferry, the annual Byers Green Water Carnival took place. Events such as canoe racing, quoits and the greasy pole were popular with the large crowds and open air dancing took place. The carnivals came to an end around 1914 at the outbreak of war.

The surviving abutment of the 1887 bridge.

*The Jubilee Bridge of 1887 erected by the Auckland District Highway Board.
Courtesy of Tom Hutchinson.*

Dedication plates for the old and new Jubilee Bridges.

Page Bank Bridge

Page Bank is a former colliery village situated on the north bank of the River Wear whose pit opened in 1851. At the site of an old tolled ford a colliery rail bridge was erected in 1853, the structure resting on seven sets of four wooden piles probably driven into the banks and bed of the river. In 1947 it was converted into a single lane road bridge. In November 1967 during flooding, the bridge support structure was badly damaged and the bridge was closed. At this time many of the residents moved away and the houses became derelict and were demolished in the early 1970s.

A new bridge was finally erected slightly downstream in 1995. Its engineer and designer was David Newbegin, Director of the Environment for Durham County Council, and the contractor was John Mowlem Construction plc. The Right Hon Tony Blair MP officially opened the bridge on 17th May 1996.

At the site of the original rail and road structure are the remains of what is

thought to be a Roman bridge. Its existence was revealed in the drought of 1995. The bridge is thought to have served a Roman road between Sunderland and Binchester via Houghton and Old Durham.

Further downstream at Spring Bank near Tudhoe the site of an old ford exists, which is also said to be Roman in origin.

Left: The new Page Bank Bridge of 1995.

The Page Bank Rail Bridge of 1853 before its conversion to a road bridge. Courtesy of Tom Hutchinson.

Page Bank Bridge under conversion from rail to road bridge. Courtesy of Bob Abley.

Croxdale Viaduct

On 15th September 1872 a new section of the main rail line from London to Newcastle was opened to the south east of Sunderland Bridge. A junction at Tursdale was created to enable a brand new stretch of line to veer north west away from the old Leamside Line, passing Hett Village and crossing the River Wear via a brand new viaduct at Croxdale.

The viaduct was constructed between 1871 and 1872 under the supervision of railway engineer Thomas Elliot Harrison. It is 230 yards in length, 75 feet high and contains 11 elliptical arches each of 60 feet span. Unlike earlier stone viaducts in County Durham, Croxdale is of red brick construction but the bases of its piers are of natural stone. The coming of the railways to Sunderland Bridge resulted in the development of coal mining in the area and the Weardale Iron and Coal Company opened Croxdale Colliery or Thornton Pit as it was sometimes known in 1875. The viaduct is still in regular use today as a main line rail bridge.

Croxdale Viaduct erected 1871/1872.

Sunderland Bridge

The village of Sunderland Bridge, like the city at the mouth of the River Wear, was so called because it was created on sundered or separated land, in this instance land separated from the rest of the parish of St Oswald by the river. At some point it was thought necessary to add 'bridge' to its name to avoid confusion with its larger namesake.

A stone bridge of some description is said to have existed here since the 13th century and carried the Great North Road. It is said that King David of Scotland made plans to hide under the arches of this bridge whilst fleeing from his defeat at the Battle of Neville's Cross in 1346. A bridge of the 15th century is thought to have had three arches, but the present bridge of four arches was probably erected a century later. The existing bridge required strengthening in 1722 and again in 1750 when its abutments were undermined. The southern arch of the bridge collapsed in May 1769 and was completely rebuilt and within a short period of time, the northern arch suffered the same fate and needed reconstructing. The two original centre arches are consequently the only ones to display their original five-ribbed design. The bridge stands 18 feet in width between its parapets.

In 1760 it is recorded that a mail coach was delayed at the bridge because of flooding and the mail had to be transferred to horseback. The entire bridge was widened and provided with higher parapets in 1822 after another mail coach overturned 'owing to the driver taking too wide a turn on entering the bridge to avoid a groom who was taking the same turn on horseback'. Two coach passengers were thrown off the bridge and killed.

The present bridge at Sunderland Bridge, thought to have been erected in the 16th century.

Croxdale Bridge on the A167

At a time of road improvement schemes the Croxdale A167 Bridge was erected around 1924. It was sited some 200 yards downstream of the historic stone Sunderland Bridge to protect the old structure from the increasing traffic of the day. During its construction a flood occurred on 1st June 1924 that swept away

building materials and damaged the newly constructed foundations of the bridge. The structure is similar in design and age to the Lambton Road Bridge at Chester-le-Street.

Some two miles downstream of Croxdale's A167 Bridge stands the site of an old ford at Low Butterby, which is known for its fortified medieval farmhouse and moat.

Croxdale Bridge on the A167, constructed around 1924.

Houghall Colliery Rail Bridge

Durham's first railway station opened in Shincliffe Village on 28th June 1839. It was the western terminus of a rail line from Sunderland that had been built by the Sunderland Dock Company some eight years earlier. After the sinking of Houghall Colliery in 1840 a wagonway was constructed from the pit to Shincliffe Station, which crossed the River Wear via a wooden rail bridge. The first coals were shipped over the river in 1842, so the bridge dates to this time. The wagonway was eventually extended south west from Houghall to Croxdale Colliery via Pinnock Hill and Low Burnhall.

From 1842 until 1886, coal wagons were rope hauled across the bridge on an embankment to be transferred via the Sunderland and Durham Railway to

the Port of Sunderland. Boreholes drilled below the Hutton Seam of Houghall Colliery in 1880 proved its lower coals to be worthless and the fate of the pit was sealed. The bridge was dismantled after the collieries using it closed, but a natural stone abutment still remains at the river's edge.

A surviving abutment of Houghall Colliery Rail Bridge, built around 1842.

Shincliffe Bridge

The village of Shincliffe is often associated with ghosts and trolls. Whether the trolls ever guarded the bridges at Shinclffe however is for another publication. The ancient name for the village was in fact 'Scinna Cliffe' which means 'hill of the ghost or demon'.

It is thought that the first bridge at Shincliffe was in existence as early as 1200, but despite repairs in the 1300s, it was in a state of ruin by the end of the century. Bishop Skirlaw built a new bridge around 1400, which is said by Surtees to have survived for the next 350 years. Leland however writing around 1540 suggests that this bridge collapsed some two or three years earlier. In the flood of February 1753 two arches of the bridge were swept away and a complete pillar fell into the river without breaking. Despite repairs the bridge was again in need of replacement by the 1820s.

The existing bridge was condemned as being too narrow and out of repair by County Surveyor Ignatius Bonomi and he designed a new stone bridge for the village to be built just downstream of the old structure. The building of the bridge commenced in June 1824 and was opened in 1826, when the old medieval bridge was promptly dismantled. This present bridge consists of two flat elliptical arches each of 60 feet span, with a causeway arch at the Shincliffe end 20 feet in width. The cost of building the bridge was £7,056 7s 6d. A steel beamed footbridge was attached to the structure on the upstream side of the bridge sometime in the 20th century.

In November 1967, water rose to within 18 inches of the top of the arches and the bridge was observed to be 'vibrating alarmingly'. Having survived this recent incident, the bridge stands today as a fine example of early 19th century engineering.

Shincliffe Bridge of 1826, designed by Ignatius Bonomi.

A print by Joseph Bouet showing the medieval bridge at Shincliffe, which was erected around 1400. In the foreground, men work to establish the foundations of Bonomi's replacement bridge. A horse-powered pumping mechanism removes excess water from a wooden enclosure on the bank of the river. The medieval bridge was demolished when the new structure was completed in 1826. Reproduced by permission of Durham University Library.

Maiden Castle Footbridge

Maiden Castle Footbridge lies close to the ancient hill fort that gives it its name and was designed by Ove Arup and Partners. The bridge opened in 1974. It is a steel cable-stayed single span footbridge of fan arrangement with an inclined pylon. Its overall length is 61 metres. The bridge design is similar to the Millennium Footbridge further down the river. Close to this modern steel structure is the site of what is thought to have been a timber Roman bridge. Surtees mentions the bridge in an archaeological report of 1785 as follows.

'During the late dry summer, the wooden piers of a bridge over the Wear leading exactly to the station at Old Durham were not only visible, but those very piers left high and dry were taken up consisting of long trunks of trees, squared and bored and mortised together so as to form a strong foundation on each side of the river'. The Roman bridges in Old Durham and Kepier are thought to be the places at which an old Roman road crossed the River Wear on its way north to Hadrian's Wall.

Maiden Castle Footbridge of 1974.

Rail Bridge to Old Elvet Station

In March 1892 work commenced on an extension line for the Sunderland to Durham rail service. As part of the scheme, an iron rail bridge of one large elliptical arch was erected near Hollow Drift to carry the line across the Wear to the newly constructed railway station of Elvet.

T.D. Ridley of Middlesbrough were contractors for the structure, which was built for a total outlay of £30,000. Stockton Forge fabricated the ironwork of the bridge at a cost of £5,000. The foundations were sunk three to four feet below the bed of the river. When partially erected the structure was swept away during a flood, which delayed the project by one month. The bridge when completed was 130 feet long and weighed 130 tons.

The line opened a week before Miners' Gala Day on 25th July 1893. Optimistically, the approaches to the bridge had been made double width for a possible second line. In the event passenger services were only operated until 1931, when the line became 'goods only' until its eventual closure in 1949. Despite the demise of the line, it was opened once per year for the following four years on Miners' Gala Day to bring passengers from Sunderland into Durham City for 'The Big Meeting'. Elvet Station was demolished in 1963 and the fate of the rail bridge was sealed. Only the red brick abutments of the bridge now stand on each side of the river.

Close to the rail bridge at the place where Green Lane approaches the river from Elvet, is the site of an old ford. Just downstream on the west side of the river is the site of the Durham Racecourse. Horse racing took place here between 1733 and 1887 in an area called 'Smithyhaughs' and like the Bishop Auckland meetings upstream, temporary footbridges were sometimes erected across the river for access to the event. It is recorded that, 'At the Durham Races of 4th August 1769 a temporary bridge was laid over the Wear near the Race Ground which fell down with about 50 people on it, but the water being very shallow no lives were lost nor did any ill consequences follow except for the loss of hats wigs and a ducking.'

The Old Elvet Rail Bridge of 1892. Courtesy Michael F. Richardson.

In May of 1849 on the Durham Racecourse, a cricket match took place between an 'All England Eleven' and Durham City Cricket Club, when as in 1769, a temporary wooden trestle footbridge was installed for the event. The scene, complete with bridge, was captured in a drawing that appeared in the *Illustrated London News*.

The temporary footbridge at the England vs Durham City Cricket Club match of 1849.

Baths Bridge

The first wooden footbridge on this site was built in 1855 a year after the baths themselves were erected. At this time however the structure was commonly known as the Pelaw-Leazes Bridge. In 1894 the following is recorded in the *History, Topography and Directory of Durham* for that year. 'The want of communication between Elvet and Gilesgate has long been felt by the inhabitants of the City and it is in contemplation to erect a new bridge close to the baths for accommodation of those visiting them as well as for the convenience of the inhabitants of Elvet and the south end of Durham, as the present wooden structure is considered to be unsafe.'

In 1898 a wrought iron footbridge was erected on the site at a cost of £700, making use of the same abutments.

A reinforced concrete single span footbridge was then constructed in the early 1960s. The consultants were L.G. Mouchel and Partners and the contractors Purbie Lumsdon and Co. The City Engineer was L.E. Ellis. Councillor J.O. Luke, Chairman of the Works Committee of the City Council, formerly opened the bridge on 16th June 1962.

The wooden Bath Bridge of 1855. Courtesy Michael F. Richardson.

The wrought iron Baths Bridge of 1898 on Regatta Day. Courtesy Michael F. Richardson.

New Elvet Road Bridge

In October 1960 radical and controversial plans were unveiled to improve the movement and control of road traffic around Durham and protect its historic city centre. Contained within these plans was the construction of two new road bridges across the River Wear, with an underpass at Claypath to link them both together.

New Elvet Bridge was the second of these two new road bridges to be opened within the scheme. The bridge was designed by County Engineer Mr John Tully and was built at a cost of £500,000. Although conceived in 1961 it was not erected until 1975 and opened to traffic the following year. The construction of this bridge and associated road system resulted in the demise of the fondly remembered police traffic control box in Durham City market place.

The Concrete Society in its annual awards praised the bridge for the manner in which it blended with other modern structures in the area without clashing with the older buildings.

The New Elvet Bridge of 1975. Browns Boathouse was restored complete with its sloping walls in 2004.

Old Elvet Bridge

Bishop Hugh Pudsey built Old Elvet Bridge as a second river crossing for the City of Durham in 1160. Before this date the ancient area of Elvet was connected to the peninsula by a ford. The Anglo-Saxon name for Elvet was Aelfet Ee, which literally means 'swan river-island'. The bridge also had an association with horses, for it connects the street of Old Elvet where the City's horse fairs were once held to Saddler Street on the peninsula side of the river.

Extensive reconstruction and repair of the bridge was required by 1228, which was carried out by Bishop Fox. Three arches of the structure were destroyed in the great flood of 1771 and they were rebuilt in the same style. Originally the bridge had 14 arches but only 10 are now visible, four of which are on dry land. The bridge was widened in 1805 from 16.4 feet to 31.2 feet when it also lost its pedestrian refuges. During this work, a coin from the reign of Edward VI (1537-1553) was uncovered in the masonry of the structure. The remains of St Andrew's Chapel (1274-1283) at the Elvet end of the bridge are now hidden under a modern shop front. At the west end of the bridge stood the Chapel of St James, which was replaced by the House of Correction. An infamous Northumbrian piper called Jamie Allan was held captive in the House of Correction until his death and it is said that his pipes can still sometimes be heard at night around the bridge. The structure was re-surfaced in sandstone by the City Council in 1978, and is now pedestrian only.

A north view of Old Elvet Bridge with the remains of St Andrew's Chapel to the right.

Kingsgate Bridge

The delicate high level footbridge of Kingsgate was designed by Sir Ove Arup and was opened to the public in November of 1963. It was innovatively created in two concrete sections, each built parallel to the riverbank. When completed the sections were swung together from each side to meet at the river centre. The parapets of the bridge actually form its structural members. It was jointly financed by the University and City and was built at a cost of £36,000 to connect the peninsula with University developments in New Elvet to the east of the river. In 1993 it won a mature concrete structures award from the Concrete Society. The futuristic appearance of the bridge, however, has not always met with public approval.

Sir Ove Arup (1895-1988) was born in Newcastle to Danish parents. Despite his involvement in prestigious developments such as the Sydney Opera House, Coventry Cathedral and the Barbican throughout his life, he conceded that his favourite work of design had been the Kingsgate Bridge in Durham.

The Kingsgate Bridge of 1963: Sir Ove Arup's favourite design work.

Prebends Bridge

Originally a ford and ferry connected the Cathedral peninsula to the other side of the river at this site, but around 1574 a wooden footbridge on stone piers was erected. The Treasurer's Book of 1568 refers to the building of the stone piers: 'three masons came to worke upon the bridge that shall be made, 12 shillings'. The wooden structure was replaced by a narrow stone footbridge in 1696, which was washed away except for its abutments in the great flood of November 1771. It is documented that 'the water rose 8 feet 10 inches higher than had ever been recorded in the annals of Durham' during this flood. The western abutment of the 1696 stone structure still survives today.

Just downstream from the above site the present Prebends Bridge was built between 1772 and 1778 using local sandstone, having been designed for the Dean and Chapter by George Nicholson. A 'prebend' is the land from which a prebendary of canon derives his income. In 1778/9 Baileygate was created to accommodate carriage traffic wishing to make use of the new bridge, but only prebends and canons of the Cathedral have the authority to take a vehicle over it. The bridge with its three semicircular segmental arches and balustraded battlement was restored in 1955/56. Sir Walter Scott's thoughts of Durham were placed on an oak panel and attached to the bridge, but a stone tablet encased in the north west wall has now replaced it.

> *Grey towers of Durham*
> *Yet well I love thy mixed and massive piles*
> *Half church of God half castle 'gainst the Scots*
> *And long to roam these venerable isles*
> *With records stored of deeds long since forgot.*

Framwellgate Bridge

Framwellgate Bridge was built around 1128 by Bishop Ranulf Flambard as the city's first permanent river crossing and was known until the 16th century as 'Old Bridge'. Flambard was one of the most powerful men in Durham, becoming Bishop in 1099 because of his successful role as a tax collector for King William Rufus. His original bridge may have had up to six arches. The area of Framwellgate is named after a well in Durham market place, which stood where the statue of King Neptune now resides.

In 1401 the bridge was re-built by Bishop Thomas Langley after damage by flooding. The cost of rebuilding came in part from the tolls raised via a temporary ferry. The two main arches of 90 feet span seen today are thought to date from this later construction, but a third smaller arch hidden beneath the buildings of Silver Street may belong to Flambard's original structure. A chapel occupied the central portion of the bridge. Originally towers and gates defended each end of the bridge but one tower and gate were removed before the 16th century, and the other in 1760.

The bridge itself survived the great flood of 1771 although two houses on the end of the bridge were destroyed. When the battlements were being removed in 1828, a live toad is said to have been found encapsulated within the masonry of the bridge! According to a Local Board of Health Report, a motion was passed on 6th July 1859 to improve the bridge when it was widened from 21.6 feet to 28.2 feet. The carriageway was resurfaced in sandstone by the City Council in 1977 and the bridge is now pedestrian only.

The Framwellgate Bridge being widened in 1859. Courtesy Michael F. Richardson.

Milburngate Road Bridge

Following the unveiling of plans in 1960 to rearrange the movement of traffic around the City of Durham the first of two new river crossings, Milburngate Bridge, was opened in 1967. The overall scheme had proved somewhat controversial at its planning stage, as parts of the old city would disappear.

There was conjecture that the scheme would affect businesses in the city even though a new shopping centre for Milburngate had been incorporated into the plans.

The structure was designed by Durham County Council and built by Holst and Company. It is a balanced cantilever bridge, with a suspended span design of reinforced concrete with pre-cast, pre-stressed concrete beams. The span lengths are 20.70 metres, 47.78 metres, 20.70 metres and 9.14 metres.

The bridge and its approaches were opened on 3rd April 1967 by Councillor S.C. Docking JP, Chairman of the Durham County Council, at a ceremony presided over by the Mayor, Councillor Mrs M.A. Thornhill MA JP.

Milburngate Bridge opened in 1967.

Millennium or Penny Ferry Footbridge

The Millennium Bridge as its name suggests is one of the newest structures to span the River Wear, having been planned as a foot and cycle bridge for the 21st century. The bridge opened in April of 2002 and its funding came via the National Lottery. The bridge is of the cable-stayed type. The public were asked to choose a name for the new structure and it was consequently renamed the Penny Ferry Bridge after an old ferry which operated close by.

Around half a mile downriver from one of the newest bridges on the Wear is the site of one of its very oldest structures. A Roman bridge is thought to have existed on the bend of the river close to Kepier medieval hospital. There is also conjecture that a second Roman structure may have been sited some 200 yards further downstream again.

Half a mile further downriver, close to Frankland Park Farm, a ford is shown on a mid 19th century map.

The Millennium or Penny Ferry Foot and Cycle Bridge of 2002.

Miners' Footbridge, Kepier Woods

A rope suspension footbridge once stood over the Wear at Kepier Woods. Miners used the bridge to cross the river when they worked at the various drift mines in the area. It is thought to have been erected around 1915 and was still in use in 1925. It is said that the concrete blocks that supported the structure are only visible on the riverbank in dry weather, but a block can be seen on the eastern bank that may have belonged to the bridge.

During the General Strike of 1926 pitmen opened up the workings to provide coal for their families. The drift mines of Kepier Woods were still being operated into the 1930s and coal tubs were pulled around their tracks by steel ropes. Today the area is a pleasant riverside walk, but there are still signs of mine working in the woods where the small stonewalls leading into the drifts from the towpaths can be seen. It is thought that the suspension bridge may have survived into the 1950s.

The Miners' Rope Bridge in Kepier Woods, photographed around 1925. Courtesy Michael F. Richardson.

Belmont Viaduct

The Belmont Viaduct was constructed in 1856 at Kepier Woods to take main line rail traffic across the River Wear from Brasside to Belmont. It also carried coal over the river from Framwellgate Moor Colliery. The architect is thought to have been Richard Cail. The Leamside Line was originally part of the main London to Newcastle rail service until 1872 when it was re-routed north at Newton Hall, removing the necessity for the line to cross the river at this point. Use of the 'old main line' gradually declined thereafter and by the 1960s the rail track on the bridge had been lifted. The viaduct is 694 feet long, has nine arches each of 60 feet span and stands 130 feet above river level. Ancient mine workings had to be shored up with brickwork set in Roman cement before its foundations could be established. Ashlar stone for the structure came from the quarries of Claxtons, Leam, Penshaw, Benton and Rudchester. The interiors of the arches were made of brickwork, the bricks being made 'on the spot by steam machinery'. The weight of the completed viaduct was estimated to be 35,000 tons.

The Society of Antiquaries offered the following commentary at the time. 'If the moon be inhabited and the Lunarians are in possession of a telescope equal in power to Lord Rosse's, the Belmont Viaduct will be palpable to their eyes and must make them feel a little proud of the planet to which, for better or worse, they are indissolubly attached.'

Brasside Bridge

From the 1840s a wooden rail bridge crossed the river at this site. The bridge carried the Lambton Railway lines from the local collieries of Framwellgate Moor, Frankland and Brasside, to the main Leamside Line to the east of the river at Rainton Crossing. A 'self-acting' incline led the coal wagons to the bridge. Despite the building of Belmont Viaduct and a new associated line in 1856, Frankland and Brasside Collieries continued to use the old wooden bridge. Brasside Bridge was still present in 1914 when it is said that the Durham Light Infantry used it and the surrounding area for army manoeuvres.

In 1935 Sunderland and South Shields Water Company used what may have been the surviving natural stone abutments to carry twin 30 inch water mains across the river as part of its Burnhope Pipeline. A bowstring iron footbridge with wooden tread boards was later built over the abutments and water mains possibly around 1950. It still survives today, although the bridge is in poor order.

The place name of Brasside is said to have evolved from 'Bradside' meaning broad hillside.

The pipe/footbridge at Brasside.

The Toll Bridge, Finchale

A hermitage existed at Finchale before its priory was built in the 13th century. The toll bridge over the river, however, was not erected until 1937. Before this, access from the Cocken Road was by the Finchale Ferry or stepping-stones. The eccentric St Godric who is buried in the priory may not have made much use of the stepping-stones, for he is said to have regularly lain in the River Wear throughout winter nights with the freezing water up to his neck! The devil is believed to have often run off with his clothes, but a mischievous farmer may have been the true culprit. The place name of Finchale is thought to have an ornithological derivation, being 'the dale inhabited by the finches'. The 'fink' pronunciation within Finchale is said to actually mimic the sound that this bird makes.

English Heritage originally owned the 20th century bridge and a toll of one penny was required to cross it. In later years a penny slot gate was installed at the end of the bridge to collect tolls. The bridge is the original structure on the site but has been refurbished several times throughout its life. It has concrete abutments and piers with steel beams and timber decking and parapets. Ownership of the bridge was taken over by Durham County Council in 1996. The bridge became toll free in the 1970s.

A large weir is thought to have been erected by the Romans upstream of the Finchale Toll Bridge. It is shown on an old woodcut of 'A West View of Finchale Priory', which Nathaniel Buck carved for Ralph Carr Esq in 1728.

Cocken Bridge

Cocken Bridge crosses the river close to Low Cocken Farm around two miles west of Finchale Priory and stands close to the site of an old ford. It is a single span lattice girder iron bridge 120 feet in length and has an inside width of 20 feet. It was opened on Tuesday 27th April 1886 by a 'Miss Boyd', and was built at a total cost of £3,400.

The perils of fords in times of flooding are highlighted by the drowning of two servants from Cocken House, whom we are told died whilst attempting to cross Cockenford at the time of the great flood of 17th November 1771.

Three quarters of a mile downstream of Cocken Bridge lies the site of Old Mill Ford and stepping-stones. A further 100 yards downriver is the site of a second set of stepping-stones.

Cocken Bridge, opened 27th April 1886.

New Lumley Bridge on the B1284

The Prime Minister, the Rt Hon Tony Blair MP officially opened New Lumley Bridge on 14th November 1997. Durham County Council designed the structure and the engineer was David Newbegin, Director of Environment and Technical Services. The contractor was John Mowlem Construction plc. The reinforced concrete deck of the bridge rests on large steel beams and its spans are 25 metres, 75 metres and 25 metres.

The distinctive blue painted beams of the bridge contrast boldly with the green of the surrounding countryside and the buff sandstone of Lumley Castle. It was erected to replace an early 20th century lattice girder narrow bridge located just downstream.

New Lumley Bridge, opened 14th November 1997.

Old Lumley Road Bridge

Old Lumley Road Bridge was erected close to the entrance of Lumley Castle and was formally opened by T.C. Renwick in October of 1914. Its construction entailed the use of a steel trough deck with lattice girders supported on steel cross beams, all resting on stone abutments and centre pier. The designer is thought to have been Durham County Council and the bridge was erected at a total cost of £17,600.

A new road system accompanied the construction of the bridge and a payment had to be made to the Earl of Scarborough to compensate for the loss of toll bridge earnings. In 1964 a footbridge was added to the structure, which resulted in the demolition of the Penny Ferry Footbridge just downstream.

The bridge was demolished save for the abutments around 1997, when a replacement structure to carry the B1284 was erected.

A surviving abutment of Old Lumley Bridge.

LUMLEY BRIDGE, CHESTER-LE-STREET.

Old Lumley Bridge shortly after construction.

Penny or Halfpenny Bridge, Chester-le-Street

There is some conjecture as to whether this bridge was called the Penny Bridge or the Halfpenny Bridge. Whatever its name it was erected on the site of the old rope-haul Lumley Ferry around 100 yards upstream of the fast water. It was an iron footbridge with a diamond shaped open pattern to its sides and wooden tread-boards. Pylon style four-post metal piers supported the bridge at each riverbank. A concrete plinth on the east bank is now all that survives of the structure.

Richard Nelson, 1st sextant of Great Lumley Church, tells us in his notebook 'the new bridge at Lumley Ferry was opened by the Earl of Scarborough, his mother the Countess and his sister the Marchioness of Zetland and others, on December 9th 1898'.

The bridge gave foot access to Lumley Castle from Chester-le-Street but was also used by pitmen on their way to work in the Lumley Collieries. It is said that the old pitmen's path to the east of the bridge can still be observed in dry weather. The County Council bought the bridge in 1950 for £200.

A popular bathing area existed close to the bridge which was continuously replenished by river water. Eager bathers often used the bridge railings somewhat unwisely to jump into the river. The bridge was demolished in 1964 after a cantilever footpath was added to the nearby Lumley Bridge of 1914.

The bridge was erected close to the site of what is thought to be the Roman logistics fort of 'Concangis'. On the river itself a Roman dam is said to have been constructed in an area just downstream of this structure and a Roman bridge may have once existed in the vicinity.

Lumley Ford was also sited around 400 yards downstream of the footbridge. Its presence is shown on a map of 1787.

Penny or Halfpenny Bridge, Chester-le-Street, opened 9th December 1898. The area downstream of the bridge was popular with bathers.

A1M Motorway Bridge

Travers Morgan and Partners designed the A1M Motorway Bridge. It has an 'in-situ' reinforced concrete voided slab deck set on reinforced concrete V shaped piers and abutments founded on steel piles. The river was temporarily diverted to carry out the construction work 'on the dry' then returned to its natural course when the bridge was completed. The bridge opened in 1968.

The A1M Motorway Bridge at Chester-le-Street, opened in 1968.

Lambton Road Bridge on the A183

Lambton Road Bridge was constructed between 1924 and 1926 to improve communications between Sunderland and Chester-le-Street. The plan effectively took traffic away from the historic 15th century Chester New Bridge, whose sole task now is to provide access to the Lambton Estate.

Lambton Bridge is similar in design and dates to the same period as Croxdale Bridge on the A167. The contractor was Sir Robert McAlpine and the designer is thought to have been Durham County Council. The bridge has stone faced concrete abutments and piers, with a steel trough deck on steel beams, and cast iron parapets.

Lambton Road Bridge on the A183, opened in 1926.

Chester New Bridge

This fine 15th century bridge of four arches is a scheduled ancient monument and still remains for the most part in its original form, although it was stated to be 'in decay' in January of 1565. Its span is around 180 feet and is 16 feet in width. The bridge has no footpath. The stone ramp on which it is built is the modern spring tidal limit of the Wear, being 10 miles from the rivermouth. Until the end of the 18th century it was the most easterly bridge that stood over the river.

In 1644 the Scottish Army crossed this bridge on their way to Sunderland. One man who never quite achieved this feat was one Charles Swinburne. He came down Newbridge Bank at speed on horseback around 1860 and did not quite make the sharp left turn onto the bridge safely. Both horse and rider were killed in their plunge over the parapet into the river below. His name and a date commemorate the tragedy on the northern parapet of the bridge. It is known as 'Swinburne's Leap'.

The Royal Engineers mined the western pillar of the bridge in the 1940s in anticipation of a possible German invasion, and the holes can still be observed today.

At the east end of the bridge is a tall arched gateway of 1815 designed by Ignatius Bonomi. The Lambton family crest is carved onto the gateway, whose large remote controlled iron gates give access to the estate from the west.

Just downstream of Chester New Bridge are the remains of a Saxon Ford and Chapel. Its name is Bruggeford, 'brugge' being the Saxon name for a bridge. It is sloped to assist the passage of water downstream. The ford has suffered

The 15th century Chester New Bridge, Chester-le-Street.

erosion towards its centre but can still be seen at low tide.

There is a suggestion that an earlier structure existed on the site of Chester New Bridge in the 14th century. In August of 1314 Lord Lambton made a presentation to the Chapel of Bruggeford and according to the historian Surtees 'the shell of this oratory lately stood near the new bridge within the entrance of Lambton Park'.

Lamb Bridge on the Lambton Estate

Lamb Bridge is the first of the two private bridges within the Lambton Estate. Ignatius Bonomi designed the bridge and its foundation stone was laid in September of 1819. This beautiful single span (82.5 feet) humped-backed stone built bridge sits in the splendid isolation of Lambton Woods. The sculpture of a resting lamb on a stone plinth sits on each of the four corners of the bridge. The stone parapets on the structure are still complemented by the original cast iron railings on the approaches to the bridge. The name Lambton is of Saxon origin, and actually means 'estate of the lambs'.

Lambton Castle has been much affected by subsidence due to coal mining during its recent history and Lamb Bridge may have been similarly affected. A sign on the bridge warns that it is unsafe for heavy traffic, and a weight limit of 1.5 tonnes gross and a speed limit of 5 mph have been imposed on estate traffic. The bridge stands at the normal tidal limit of the River Wear.

Above: Lamb Bridge on the Lambton Estate designed by Ignatius Bonomi and erected in 1819.

Right: A lamb rests on one of the four corners of the bridge.

New Bridge on the Lambton Estate

The River Wear broadly dissects the Lambton Estate in a west to east direction. Access to the estate from both sides of the river is available at several points around its perimeter including entry via the 15th century New Bridge. Crossing the river within the estate itself means the use of one of two private bridges. The most westerly of the two is Lamb Bridge which because of its age and fragility has had a weight and speed restriction placed upon it for many years. The bridge to the east near Scorers Wood is New Bridge, which may have been erected to handle the heavier transport that is now required to work and manage the estate. This structure and its associated access from Black Drive are shown to be in place on an Ordnance Survey map of 1932, but

New Bridge on the Lambton Estate.

not on a map of 1862. A resident of the estate remembers the bridge being present in 1927. The body of the bridge is metal in construction and the two abutments of natural stone dressed blocks suggest a build date around the turn of the 20th century.

Of interest slightly upstream of this bridge is the ruin of an arch immediately adjacent to the river on the south bank, with old wooden piles in the water below it. This could be the remains of an early bridge or a quay from the days when the river was navigated by keelboats as far upstream as Picktree.

Around half a mile downstream of New Bridge are the sites of the ford and ferry of Biddick.

The ruin of an arch on the Lambton Estate. New Bridge can be seen downstream.

Chartershaugh Bridge

Chartershaugh Bridge (sometimes called Chaytorshaugh) was designed by Travers Morgan and built by Mowlem Construction. It was erected in 1975 to improve connections between Washington and Houghton-le-Spring and became the main route between the two towns to fulfil the role that Fatfield or Penshaw Bridge had been designed for some 86 years previously.

It is a three span bridge with simple supported beams and reinforced composite concrete deck. Its overall length is 103.6 metres.

It bears the name of the small mining village that existed just to the west of the bridge that was demolished in the 1970s during the development of Washington New Town. Biddick Ford provided an early crossing point nearby and an inn once stood close to the river called the Ferryboat Tavern, confirming that Biddick Ferry also once served the village here. The ferry can be seen on a map of 1787 and its approach on the west side of the river still survives to this day.

The great flood of 1771, which was ruinous to many bridges over the Wear, totally deluged Chartershaugh Colliery rendering it idle for 74 years. Two other local collieries, however, took their coals by wagonway to Chartershaugh for river transport to Sunderland. These were the Beamish Mary Pit and Harraton Colliery.

Chartershaugh Bridge in Washington, erected in 1975. The site of the Biddick Ferry is to the centre of the picture.

Fatfield or Penshaw Bridge

The Fatfield or Penshaw Bridge was built in 1889 at a cost of £8,000. It was designed by D. Balfour of Houghton in 1888, and constructed by Head Wrightson. The Earl of Durham officially opened the bridge on the 29th January 1890. It is a single span structure with a bowstring riveted truss and wrought iron girders. Its ashlar masonry abutments rest on 12 inch timber piles. It has a 157.5 feet span, a 16.7 feet road width and a 4.5 feet wide footway. It was designed to take the main road traffic of the day from Washington to Houghton-le-Spring.

Along this stretch of the Wear, riverside hostelries like the Biddick Inn were much frequented by the keelmen throughout the 18th and 19th centuries whilst their keels were being loaded with coals. Most have now been demolished or converted into private residences.

Nearby stands the small promontory of Worm Hill, which locals believe is the hill around which the 'Lambton Worm wrapped its tail ten times' in the famous Wearside ballad of that name. Intriguingly, it has been suggested that the origin of the legend of the Lambton Worm stems from the sighting of the dragon-headed prow of a Viking long ship that long ago sailed up the River Wear here. The Saxon word for dragon is actually 'wurm'.

A quarter of a mile downstream of Penshaw Bridge lies the site of an old ferry in an area once known as Penshaw Staithes. A slipway at the site of the ferry on the north side of the river still survives today. In past times another option was available to cross the river here. The numerous coal-laden keelboats had to wait for high tide to make their journey to the rivermouth and it is said that it was once possible to cross the river in this area at certain times by stepping from keel to keel.

From early in the 18th century coal wagons travelled down inclines along wooden and iron rail tracks to Penshaw Staithes from many of the surrounding collieries. The coal was then transferred from its jetties into the waiting keelboats, the empty wagons or chaldrons being hauled back to the collieries by horses. At this time the river was the only means to get coal to the port at Sunderland. The invention of the steam locomotive then the development of main line railways from the 1820s however, sounded the death knell for the keelmen who worked the tidal reaches of the river.

The community of Penshaw Staithes no longer survives today, having been absorbed into an area now known as Mount Pleasant. Bobby Thompson the much-loved North East comedian was born in Penshaw Staithes.

Penshaw or Fatfield Bridge from the vantage point of Worm Hill. The Biddick Inn can be seen in the foreground, and Penshaw Monument is to the rear left of the picture.

The surviving slipway at Penshaw Staithes Ferry close to the houses of South View.

The Victoria Viaduct, Penshaw

At early meetings of the Durham Junction Railway Company, a bridge to carry rail traffic over the River Wear at Penshaw was high on the agenda. Railway engineer Thomas Elliot Harrison favoured the erection of an iron bridge to carry road, rail and foot traffic and architect John Green of Newcastle drew up plans accordingly. These plans were rejected however in favour of a stone viaduct. The Marquis of Londonderry owned Penshaw Quarry, which could supply the stone from which a viaduct would be constructed. The fact that he also owned the coal that the railway company wanted the transportation contracts for, may provide the explanation for the rejection of the iron bridge.

As a consequence Messrs G. Walker and Burgess prepared plans for a magnificent stone viaduct. It is said that the inspiration for its design came from a Roman bridge built by Emperor Trajan in Alantara, Spain around AD 105. John Gibb & Son of Aberdeen submitted their tender for its construction to the railway company on 13th November 1835. The bridge was erected between 1836 and 1838 under the supervision of railway engineer Mr Harrison, making use of the local sandstone from Penshaw Quarry. Aberdeen granite, however, was used to strengthen the outer quoins of the large arches. The 200 masons, joiners and labourers involved in its construction worked in the most horrendous of conditions. In the early days of the contract they toiled waist deep in freezing water on a riverbed of slithering mud. As the viaduct rose upwards from the river they were exposed to the icy winds blowing from the east. Cold damp fog, which often gathers along the river here, was another hazard for them.

Just before the viaduct was completed, the temporary supports of the large north arch collapsed early one morning around 2.00 am. The noise was such that the collapse was heard five miles away in Sunderland. John Gibb tentatively examined the structure of the bridge when light permitted and to the relief of everyone concerned declared it to be undamaged. Despite this late scare the final stone was set into place on

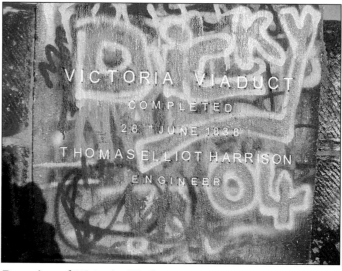

Remains of Victoria Viaduct commemorative plaque.

Coronation Day 28th June 1838 and the bridge was consequently named the Victoria Viaduct. It is considered to be one of the most impressive and beautiful stone viaducts in the country and was one of the wonders of early railway history. The total cost of construction was £40,338 5s 10d and the viaduct was opened to rail traffic on 24th August 1838.

The viaduct is 270 yards in length, 21 feet wide and stands 130 feet above river level. It contains four large main arches across the river valley and two sets of three small spans at each approach to the bridge. The widest arch of the viaduct at 160 feet was said to be the largest in Europe at the time of its construction. The remains of a 1934 plaque on the inner wall of the central parapet well on the east side of the viaduct commemorates the completion of the bridge and Mr Harrison's association with it. Despite older and more recent attempts to vandalise the inscription, it can still be deciphered.

Several flood markings or 'heights of fresh' are also chiselled into the inner side of the southern-most arch of the viaduct. Floods of 19th December 1847, 5th February 1852, 16th June 1855 and the highest of 20th September 1852 are recorded.

'Heights of fresh' or flood markings on the Victoria Viaduct.

The bridge carried the main rail line from Newcastle to London, until 1872 when the service was re-routed to the west of Durham. In later years it carried freight trains and was often used as a diversionary route when maintenance work was being carried out on the main line. Until its closure in 1991 it was said to be the oldest rail bridge still in use in England. The viaduct may once again be opened up for freight traffic in an effort to relieve congestion on the main East Coast Line.

Immediately downstream of the viaduct lies the site of Low Lambton Ferry and its steps and landing still survive on both banks of the river. This rope-haul ferry was popular with miners working at North Biddick Colliery. Until 25 years ago the ribs of its old abandoned ferryboat could be seen lying on the riverbed.

The surviving steps and landing of Low Lambton Ferry.

Just downstream at Low Lambton Staithes, building stone was transferred into keelboats from the numerous quarries in the area. Several tunnels were built along a one-mile stretch of the eastern riverbank to assist in the transfer of the quarry stone down to the Wear. Some of their stone arches can be still seen today where they enter the hillside. Penshaw Monument was erected in 1844 in memory of John George Lambton, 1st Earl of Durham, using locally quarried stone.

There is a local legend that James Drummond, 3rd Duke and 6th Earl of Perth, worked as a ferryman at Low Lambton under the name of Armstrong. It is said that he took refuge in Biddick in 1746 after being wounded in the Battle of Culloden where he had fought as a Scottish General. He married Elizabeth, the daughter of local pitman John Armstrong in 1749 and produced six children. Sadly the loss of their boathouse cottage in the great flood of 1771 and all of the family associated documents within prevented any of his descendants from ever being able to fully substantiate the story. In the early 1830s grandson Thomas Drummond failed in his attempt to regain the family title in a case heard in the House of Lords. At least four generations of Drummonds are buried in nearby Penshaw Churchyard. As recorded on a family headstone, grandson Thomas took his claim to be the rightful heir to the Earldom of Perth to the grave with him on 18th November 1873 aged 81 years. The Drummond lineage in Biddick continued thereafter and descendants still live in the region to this day.

A further half a mile downstream of Victoria Viaduct lies the site of another ferry some 100 yards before Coxgreen Footbridge.

The Drummond family graves in Penshaw Churchyard. Inset: Headstone detail of the claim by Thomas to be the rightful heir to the Earldom of Perth.

Coxgreen Footbridge

Coxgreen now lies in a tranquil rural setting but like upstream, the 18th and 19th century industries of coal mining and quarrying were once very much in evidence. Wagonways brought coal to the staithes on the riverbank and keels carried it downstream to ships waiting at the rivermouth. Ship and boat building also developed here as a consequence of the coal trade.

The Barmston Ferry operated originally at this site and functioned using a rowing boat and wire rope-haul system on a river bustling with activity. Its most regular users were perhaps the workmen of Washington Chemical Works who lived on the south side of the river and the miners and quarrymen of the area. The ferry closed in February of 1956.

The tubular steel footbridge here is a two span Stewart and Lloyd 'USK' through type truss bridge with concrete decking. It makes use of the wall of an old sandstone quay on the north side of the river for its abutment but the central pier and south side abutment are of concrete. The overall length of the bridge is 162.4 feet with a single pier in the river and its deck width is 7 feet. Tubewrights Ltd of Newport supplied the fabrications for the structure. The bridge opened 'to the delight of the residents' on 5th July 1958.

Coxgreen Footbridge, opened 5th July 1958.

One mile downriver is the site of Stewarts Quay and the abandoned Saxon village of Netherton, which was known for its 'Chaleybeat' spa well. Chaleybeat means spa water which is enriched with the salts of iron. Lord North's physician extolled the health giving properties of Chaleybeat water saying 'it cured colic, the melancholy, made the lean fat, the fat lean, killed flat worms in the belly, loosened the clammy humours of the body and dried the over moist brain'. Visitor Dr Granville thought the spring to be 'beautifully sited and wonderfully adapted as a watering place'. Netherton was once an extremely busy place and a ferry operated in the mid 19th century. This area of riverside now skirts Washington Wildfowl Park. The Barmston Forge was located just to the west of the ferry.

The river makes a sweep around Offerton Haugh some 800 yards downstream of the site of Stewarts Quay and the tiny village that bears its name sits on high ground to the south east, around three quarters of a mile away. An old track known to locals as 'Clarty Lonnen' runs directly from the village down to the river and once connected Offerton to Netherton and its ferry. A coal mine operated here from 1589 to provide fuel for the boiling of brine at Sunderland to produce salt. From the Anglo-Saxon, Offerton is said to mean 'high ford', or 'farm above the ford'. Either derivation could suggest the former presence of a ford on the river nearby. A crossing may have once existed at the end of a path from Offerton Grange Farm down to the river, but a more likely explanation for the place name lies in the fact that Offerton Lane runs from the village to the ancient river crossing site downstream at Hylton.

Several families from the village of Offerton made their living from 'hailing' on the river. When a string of keels came upriver on a late tide or when the wind was against them, the keelmen employed hailers. All the boats were made fast together and a rope thrown to the shore from the first keel. The men, women and children of the family would then lay the rope over their shoulders and 'hail' or haul the keels to the staithes at Low Lambton. By the mid 19th century the developing rail networks ensured that only a handful of keels were working the river and the hailing families were left to seek alternative employment.

Hylton Bridge

A bridge for the Hylton area was suggested as early as 1817. A suspension bridge was then proposed in the mid 19th century but the scheme never reached fruition. By 1891 yet another bridge project was suggested based on a design by local architect Frank Caws. Owners of land on the Hylton Castle Estate offered free land on the north shore for the scheme, but again the proposal failed to materialise. Over 80 more years would elapse before Hylton finally got its bridge.

Hylton Bridge, Sunderland, built 1970 to 1974. The site of the original Maling Pottery of 1762 is to the bottom left of the picture.

The Hylton A19 road bridge was constructed between 1970 and 1974. It was designed by R. Travers Morgan and built by W.C. French. It has two separate decks with steel box girders and reinforced concrete decking. Its overall length is 232 metres with a width of 28.8 metres. The opening was delayed by several months when a similarly designed box girder bridge in Australia suffered structural problems.

Immediately upstream of the A19 bridge on the north side of the river lies the site of the original Maling Pottery. William Maling of Sunderland established the pottery here in 1762. Mr Maling travelled to work everyday on horseback making use of the nearby ferry. This factory is said to have produced the first transfer printed wares in the North East of England. In July of 1815 the business was relocated to Newcastle, where at the peak of its production, it claimed to be the 'largest pottery in the world'. Low Ford or Dawson's Pottery operated slightly further downstream at Hylton on the south bank of the river.

Downstream from the Hylton Bridge lies the site of the 12th century Hylton Ferry. According to the historian Surtees, Robin, Baron of Hilton granted passage of the ferry to his Chaplain William De Hilton in 1322. By the 20th century, however, maintenance of the ferry was the responsibility of the owners of nearby Wood House Farm. It was originally known as the 'Bovis Ferry' indicating that its early use was for transporting cattle as well as passengers. It was, however, a strategic river crossing point for centuries before the building of bridges further downstream. The ferry operated using a rope-haul then later a chain-haul system and could transport the horse-drawn coaches of the day across it. The Wear keelmen protested at the high tolls imposed on them to lower the rope-haul system that enabled their boats to pass by and a keelman was killed on one occasion when the rope was not lowered. The rope and

The chain-haul ferry at Hylton which was closed around 1915. Courtesy of South Hylton Local History Society.

Above: Another view of the ferry at Hylton. The old Golden Lion public house stands near the south ferry landing.

Right: The site of the Hylton Ferry today. Foreground shows a stone, possibly of Roman origin, from Briggstones.

chain-haul systems were manually operated on the ferryboat by the turning of a large wheel connected to a drum, which drove the endless belt of rope or chain and pulled the ferry across the river. The chain ferry ceased to operate around 1915 and was superseded by a rowing boat service for 'people only' which terminated in January of 1957. Redundant ferry posts are still visible today.

At the turn of the 17th century, local landowner Baron Robert Hilton beat one of his servant boys so badly that he died of his injuries. The young boy in question was Robert Skelton whose wandering spirit became famous as 'The Cauld Lad of Hylton'. His ghostly exploits are more usually associated with Hylton Castle but it is said that he was prone to visiting the nearby ferry across the River Wear, where he would pose as the ferryman taking passengers into midstream only to swiftly vanish leaving them stranded. The border name for a weir or dam is 'cauld' as in a structure near Melrose. This has spawned a recent theory that the Cauld Lad of Hylton was named after the ancient dam site just downstream.

Hylton Briggstones

An enormous ancient structure now thought by the Northern Archaeology Group to be a Roman weir or dam was assembled downstream of the Hylton ferry site and was known locally as 'Briggstones'. It was ten feet high and twenty feet wide and built with huge locally mined dressed stones placed on oaken piles driven into the riverbed. It was angled at 45 degrees across the river from a position just downstream of the Golden Lion to approximately where the Shipwrights Inn now lies on the north shore. Another source states that it was slightly further downstream and angled around 33 degrees across the river 'to the far side of Low Ford Shipyard'. An open channel 12 feet to 14 feet wide was present on the south side of the weir, through which the river ran 'tremendously, vastly and with great rage'.

A 'low tide' map of the river produced by Burleigh and Thompson in 1737 shows the structure to still be in place at this time. Detailed depth markings on the map indicate that the dam was maintaining a raised river level four and a quarter miles upstream. The river's keelmen however, found it difficult to manoeuvre boats through the open channel of the weir and campaigned to have it dismantled. The bulk of the structure was removed in the early 1800s. Subsequent attempts were then made throughout the 19th century, to completely break up and destroy its foundations. During removal work, huge quantities of lead were discovered which had been used to render the joints of the dam watertight. Some of the voussoirs of the arches were dredged out of the Wear at this time. A plate of white metal fixed to one was found to be

The Briggstones at Hylton. How they might have looked. The line of Hylton Ferry is also shown.

engraved with a Roman inscription in raised letters IM.D.AG...AVG with S.C. or S.G. in its body. A figure of a trumpeter was preserved at nearby Hylton Castle, which was said to have once framed a gateway or other edifice of the weir. Some Roman stones still exist on the site having been used to improve the ferry step landing, but many were transported downstream to Roker and used as breakwater stones around the inner moles of the harbour.

Antiquarians of the 19th century thought this structure to be a bridge or a paved ford and some within the archaeological establishment still concur with this theory today. In recent years Mr Raymond Selkirk, a founder member of the Northern Archaeology Group, has put forward a counter premise that the ancient structure is likely to have been built as a weir rather than a ford. The river is at its deepest for several miles here and would not have been considered for the sighting of a ford. Mr Selkirk suggests that the function of the Roman weir was to make the river navigable throughout its full tidal cycle as far upstream as Chester-le-Street. This would have enabled the huge quantity of supplies and provisions that were required by the Roman Army to be brought upstream to Hylton in merchant ships, then transferred onto barges to be taken further upriver to the fort of Concangis.

There is no doubt that the structure was much used, somewhat dangerously, to ford the river. It is recorded that a Mr William Maude was drowned in 1753 whilst trying to cross it. Interestingly, the ancient name for South Hylton is 'Ford' but it is said to be derived from the ancient manor of Ford and not the river structure itself.

Queen Alexandra Bridge

Looking up river to the Queen Alexandra Bridge, Sunderland. The old Doxford's covered shipbuilding hall is to the left behind the bridge. When Doxford's was redeveloped in the 1970s the hall was the biggest covered yard in the world.

NEW BRIDGE FROM NORTH SIDE

Queen Alexandra Bridge under construction around 1907.

The Queen Alexandra Bridge was designed as a double decked road and rail bridge to improve road communications across the river and for the NER to transport coal from the Annfield Plain area to the South Docks in Sunderland. The bridge provided a connection between the Sunderland to Penshaw line on the south side of the river to the Hylton, Southwick and Monkwearmouth line on the north shore. Because of its proximity to local shipbuilding yards it was decreed that a single arch bridge was required with a minimum clearance of 85 feet above high water level. The designer was Charles A. Harrison, Chief Engineer of the NER and nephew of T.E. Harrison, engineer in charge of the erection of the Victoria Viaduct at Washington. Agreement was reached between the NER and Sunderland Corporation in 1899 to build the bridge and work started in 1905. It was uniquely built from both sides of the river at the same time and met midstream on 15th October 1908. The accuracy of construction was such that the bolting together of the two halves took less than half an hour. Sixty thousand tons of red sandstone from Locharbriggs Quarry in Dumfriesshire and 350,000 bricks set on Norwegian granite footings and piers were used in its erection. Sir William Arrol and Company, 'Bridge Builders of the World' were responsible for its construction at a total cost of £450,000. Its original budget had been £325,000 of which Sunderland Corporation had agreed to pay £146,000 towards the road deck. As costs rose, however, the council's bill increased to £200,000. The bridge is 353.75 feet in length and at 2,600 tons weight; its lattice girder construction made it the heaviest bridge ever constructed in Britain at that time. In a civil engineering paper by Buscarlet and Hunter it was stated that 'the weight of the river span is not exceeded by any existing bridge of the same length.'

Seven steam engines were collectively run over the upper deck of the bridge to test it on 3rd June 1909 just one week before it was unveiled to the public. Lord Durham was presented with a specially commissioned medal when he opened the bridge on 10th June 1909. It was exclusively revealed at the ceremony that the Queen had given special permission for it to be named after her. For the next 20 years the road bridge proved to be unpopular with motorists for a toll was requested to use it. The upper rail deck only remained open for around 12 years due to a decline in the coal trade. In 1920, only one coal train per week was using the bridge. During the Second World War the redundant upper deck was used to house searchlights and anti-aircraft guns.

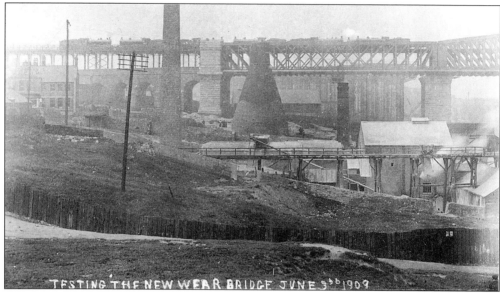

Queen Alexandra Bridge undergoing tests.

An odd tale of suspicion became associated with the bridge, for it was rumoured that it was not being fully used because there were serious faults attached to its construction. It was alleged that all of its rivets had not been put into place in order to save money! The writer's grandfather was certainly deeply suspicious of the safety of this bridge and refused to cross it throughout his life. To many observers, however, it was considered to be a remarkable feat of engineering!

Despite the bridge being granted Grade II listed status in 1984, its disused steel rail arches were controversially dismantled the following year. In March of 2005 a major overhaul of the structure commenced. The one-year contract, worth £4.5 million, was awarded to Mowlem Construction. Refurbishment work included new 'uplighting' to highlight the bridge at night and a colour change from its existing blue-grey to 'holly-green with red features.'

Half a mile downstream of the Queen Alexandra Bridge is the site of Deptford Ferry. Like Hylton upstream, this ferry operated on a coaching route to Newcastle and beyond. At Deptford, however, passengers would leave their coach on the south side of the river then resume their journey in another coach at Southwick on the north side. The approach to the ferry from Bishopwearmouth was via Wellington Lane. The ferry closed in 1909 when Queen Alexandra Bridge opened.

The opening ceremony for the Queen Alexandra Bridge, 10th June 1909. Lord Durham and other dignitaries arrived by train for the ceremony.

Sunderland Railway Bridge

Sunderland Rail Bridge, designed by Thomas Elliot Harrison, is a wrought iron box girder bowstring structure with two cross-braced ribs that are relieved by large oval strengthening webs. It is a single span design of 300 feet and its deck stands 86 feet above high tide. The rail bridge was erected immediately upstream of the road structure by the North Eastern Railway Company and leads directly to a half a mile tunnel on its way to Sunderland Station. At the time of being built it was the largest hog back iron rail bridge in the world.

The Sunderland Railway Bridge, opened in 1879.

Work started on the foundations in July of 1875 and the bridge was formally opened along with the new Central Station on the 3rd August 1879. Before its construction passengers travelling to Newcastle had to start their journey from Monkwearmouth Station on the north side of the river. It is a tribute to the designers and builders of the bridge that it has survived until 2005 without the need for major refurbishment.

A rail bridge over the Wear at Sunderland was first proposed in the 1830s to transport coal from the south side of the river to the North Dock. Isambard Kingdom Brunel, who had designed the North Dock itself, produced a design for a suitable suspension bridge. Public opinion at the time, however, was against the bridge, for it was feared that it would lead to the transport of the best coals from Wearside to Newcastle. As a consequence, the bridge was never constructed.

Brunel's suspension bridge design of the 1830s for the North Dock.

Wearmouth Bridge

The present Wearmouth Bridge with its single arch of 375 feet was erected between 1928 and 1929. It was designed by Mott, Hay and Anderson and constructed by Sir William Arrol and Company Ltd. It is a three-pinned arch bridge with two mild steel parabolic ribs on masonry faced concrete abutments. The three pinned design affords maximum flexibility, which is further enhanced by the use of spherical bearings instead of pin joints at its hinges. The overall width of the bridge is 79 feet 6 inches and it incorporates two footpaths and a roadway 48 feet across. The structure has a clearance of 85 feet and 6 inches at high tide. Parts of its balustrade come from the original bridge here and large mid span crests adorn the rails at each side of the structure bearing the words of Sunderland's motto: 'Nil desperandum auspice deo'.

To avoid traffic disruption the bridge was built around the old structure on the site. The Duke of York (later George VI) formally opened the bridge amid much pomp and ceremony on 31st October 1929. The Duke inserted the last of half a million rivets into the bridge with a riveting machine. This last ceremonial rivet was said to be made of silver and its exact position on the bridge could be pointed out by many a Wearsider. The cost of project was over £250,000.

The first bridge here with a span of 236 feet and a width of 32 feet was hailed as 'the largest single span cast iron bridge in the world'. In 1791 local MP Roland Burdon, who provided much of the finance for the venture, sought

The present day Wearmouth Bridge erected 1928 to 1929. A white cross marks the position of the ceremonial silver rivet inserted by the Duke of York.

novel ideas for a bridge to be built near the site of the Panns Ferry. He rejected the traditional materials of stone and timber in favour of the relatively untried cast iron and hired local schoolmaster Thomas Wilson to supervise its assembly. The foundation stone was laid on 24th September 1793. The stone faced abutments were founded on the limestone bluffs which are present at this point of the river and consisted of masonry rubble set in lime mortar. The bridge was uniquely constructed of cast iron 'voissoir' blocks with 105 fitted to each of the six ribs of the arch. They were connected by wrought iron straps fitted to the top, bottom and centre of each unit and then bolted together. Two hundred and sixty tons of cast iron was used in the assembly of the bridge. The deck was constructed of timber and carried a carriageway made of marl, limestone and gravel.

Before the opening ceremony a unique method of testing the bridge was conceived. One thousand foot soldiers from the Royal Tey Fencibles and the North Lincoln Militia marched across it on 18th June 1796 on their way to Whitburn to be reviewed. The bridge opened in the presence of His Royal Highness the Duke of Gloucester after a magnificent Masonic ceremony on 9th August 1796 in front of 80,000 spectators. The build costs were £41,300 and the flow of river traffic had remained undisturbed throughout its construction. A special poem was written for the occasion.

> *Ye sons of Sunderland with shouts*
> *That rival oceans roar*
> *Hail Burdon in his iron boots*
> *Who strides from shore to shore.*

In subsequent years claims were made that author and activist Thomas Paine had produced the design for the bridge and not Rowland Burdon. Paine had certainly exhibited plans for a similar structure at Paddington, but it is said that his design differed considerably from that at Wearmouth.

In 1804 engineer John Grimshaw corrected a 'declination' in the arch of the bridge of 19³/₄ inches. In his 1805 report to the Commissioners of Wearmouth Bridge he states 'It is worthy of remark that the bridge was easily thrown into great vibration by anything passing over it such as a horse, the passage of a drove of oxen, or heavy carriages; whenever this was the case, the screws and wedges could be worked far more easily and effectively at such times. Therefore the operation of straightening the arch was carried out more diligently than when it was quiescent.'

Problems associated with arch declination can be traced back to September 1795 when the bridge was

A silver bridge lottery medal of 1816.

still under construction. A sudden flood washed away a sandbank on the bed of the river below one of two timber scaffolds that had been erected to temporarily support the arch of the bridge. Although the timber support and arch were carried a few inches downriver, it was decided at that time that no readjustment was necessary. In the following eight years however, vibration and differential expansion of the arch exacerbated the problem until its correction by Mr Grimshaw in 1804.

Rowland Burdon became bankrupt in 1806 when his banking interests failed. An Act of Parliament was obtained 'enabling his assignees and other persons therein named to dispose of the securities upon the tolls of the bridge and ferry boats by way of a lottery'. The lottery took place in 1816 and boasted 150 prizes, the largest of which was £5,000. Each subscriber was given a silver medal 1³/₄ inches in diameter with a view of the bridge on one side and a commemorative inscription on the reverse.

In 1842 Michael Smith, a destitute American sailor, hatched a scheme to make money by planning to jump from the 100 feet high bridge into the River Wear. The feat took place in front of a large crowd on 15th September 1842.

By the mid 19th century serious flaws had again developed in the bridge. In 1857 it underwent a major reconstruction when engineer Robert Stephenson removed the 'hump' from the old bridge by raising the height of the abutments. He discarded the cast iron circles which formed the spandrel filling, wedged up the ribs and converted them into three box girders by plating them together in pairs. The new 'flat deck' bridge was opened to traffic on 5th March 1859 and the renovation costs were £49,104 12s 6d. None of the original cast iron voissoir blocks of the 1796 bridge are thought to have survived, but it is said that some of the ironwork in the church at Castle Eden is from the original structure.

The bridge was made free of toll for foot users in 1846 but not for vehicles and animals until November 1885.

The Burdon Bridge of 1796 and latterly the Stephenson Bridge of 1859 became famous around the world by their appearance on many thousands of pieces of Sunderland lustre pottery and glass made in the town. Mariners would often take these pieces back home with them after visiting the port.

Half a mile downstream of Wearmouth Bridge is the site of the ancient 'Sunderland' or 'Bishops' Ferry, which ran from Bodlewell Lane on the south

Robert Stephenson's flat deck road bridge of 1859 stands beyond the 1879 rail bridge, on a postcard from the early years of the 20th century. Courtesy of David Wood.

side of the river to the ferry landing at Huddleston Street, Monkwearmouth, near The Folly End. Inhabitants of the Folly End often had to move their furniture to an upstairs room whenever a ship was launched in the vicinity to avoid it getting wet! A ferry is said to have operated at this place from the 7th century, when the monks of St Peter's required access to the 'sundered' land gifted to them by King Aldfrith in 686. Until 1796 the ferry was owned by the Bishops of Durham and was leased to the Etterick family for the last 135 years of this period. On 20th April 1795 the Sunderland Ferryboat capsized and over 20 passengers were drowned. A rowing boat ferry operated until the mid 19th century then a series of steam-powered vessels ran the service from 1843 until its closure in 1957. The ferry was for foot users only and delays in getting from one side of the river to the other were common before the building of Wearmouth Bridge in 1796. Until its closure, the ferry toll of one half penny had remained unchanged for 165 years. Tenants of landowner Sir Hedworth Williamson, however, were granted free passage.

A Sunderland Ferry token. The toll of one halfpenny remained unchanged for 165 years.

In 674 Benedict Biscop built a monastery dedicated to St Peter on the northern shore of the River Wear on land given to him by King Ecgfrith. Skilled stonemasons from France and glassmakers from the continent were brought to Wearmouth to help in its construction. John the Arch-chanter of St Peter's in Rome was summoned to train the monks in music and prayer. Around 672, the Venerable Bede was born close to Wearmouth and entered the monastery at seven years of age. A further grant of land was made to Biscop in 681 to build a second part of the 'twin monastery' at Jarrow, which was dedicated to St Paul. Finally King Aldfrith gave a third portion of land to Biscop in 686 in return for a present of two silken cloaks brought from Rome. This was the separated or sundered land on the south bank of the River Wear, which eventually gave its name to the fully integrated town.

In June 716, Biscop's successor Ceolfrith took one of three exquisite bibles produced at Wearmouth to Rome to present to the Pope. Ceolfrith died in France during the journey and what happened to the bible remains unclear. Some texts say that the Pope received it from the other travelling monks, whilst another source states that the bible never reached Rome. Almost 1200 years later, near the end of the 19th century, 'The Codex Amiatinus' in the Laurentian Library in Florence was discovered to be the ancient Wearmouth Bible. It is said to be one of the most beautiful ancient manuscripts in the world. Recent research has shown that the monks of Holy Island used the Wearmouth Bible as a reference when working on the Lindisfarne Gospels between 715 and 720.

The Venerable Bede sometimes known, as 'The Father of English History' died on 27th May 735 and his remains have lain in Durham Cathedral since 1020. At St Peter's Church today, the western wall and lower portion of the tower including a porch containing eight unusual lathe-turned stone balusters all survive as part of the original monastery erected by Benedict Biscop in 674. On 24th March 2004, the City of Sunderland adopted Benedict Biscop as its patron saint.

Two additional ferries worked the last half-mile stretch of river. The first operated from steps separating the Etterick and Custom House Quays on the south side of the Wear to the Strand Quay on the north bank.

Just before the river widens into its tidal basin one final ferry service operated. The last and most easterly ferry service on the Wear worked from the Commissioners Quay near Pottery Bank to Sand Point Road in Monkwearmouth. These last two ferries are likely to have been frequently used by the workers of Sunderland employed in shipyards on the north shore.

Sunderland's bridges on 19th century local pottery. The pieces were often personalised with the buyer's or their loved one's names.

An east view of the Wearmouth Bridge of 1796, with the Lambton Coal Staithes in the foreground. The print is from a steel engraving by William Le Petite.

A mid 19th century photograph of the Wearmouth Bridge of 1796.

A modern west view of the bridges at Sunderland.

In 2005 the lead mines of Weardale are long gone and its quarries all but exhausted. The coalmines of County Durham have lain abandoned for 10 years or more. At the mouth of the Wear the great shipbuilding heritage that was Sunderland is a distant memory, cries of gulls having replaced the metallic thud of rivets and the hiss of welding torches.

The river continues its journey as it has done for centuries from source to sea, patiently waiting for the new role that it will be asked to play in the lives of the communities that surround it. If heavy industry is never to return, then perhaps its task may be to support the leisure interests of a society freed from the toll of hard physical graft. Conservation can ensure that many of the historic bridges of the Wear will continue to serve their villages, towns and cities, but an expanding and ever more mobile society will ensure that we can look forward to new bridges being erected over this fine river of ours.

The River and its Bridges in Colour

In this, the final section of the book, I have assembled a collection of colour photographs to hopefully portray the beauty of the river and its bridges. For the reader who is familiar with these scenes, I trust that the pictures provide a fitting tribute to the undoubted charm of the River Wear.

An angler casts his line in the newly formed waters of the River Wear upstream of Wearhead Bridge.

Cascading waterfalls spill downstream from Blackdene Bridge.

The block limestone shelves of Bridge End Ford, Middle Blackdene.

Broken Way Footbridge viewed through the arch of an abandoned rail bridge.

Huntshield Bridge, Ford and Stepping-Stones – three ways to cross the river.

Two wooden posts mark the pathway of an abandoned ford near Waterside House Footbridge.

Shallow Ford and Britton Bridge at Westgate.

An east view of Haswicks Bridge, Westgate.

The arching branch of a wild rose frames Brotherlee Footbridge near Westgate.

The Stone Bridge at Stanhope.

A typical summer scene around Stanhope Ford.

Looking downstream to Stanhope Central Rail Bridge from the west bank of the river.

Rogerley Rail Bridge is situated two miles downstream of Stanhope.

The Frosterley Road Bridge of 1814, which was designed by Ignatius Bonomi.

Kenneth's Bridge viewed from the high ground to the south of the river.

Kenneth's Bridge was named after a local joiner, Kenneth Maddison, who built the original structure.

The Ford and Iron Rail Bridge at Broadwood.

Looking upstream to Broadwood Road Bridge.

Wolsingham Rail Bridge as it looks today.

The remains of Brown's Bridge at Black Bank Plantation.

Low Harperley Footbridge – the only aluminium bridge on the Wear.

The modern Witton Bridge on the A68 – built to bypass the village.

Old Witton Bridge of two arches, built around 1788.

A modern downstream view of the old stone viaduct and iron road bridge at Witton Park.

The terraced houses of Bridge Street stand close to Newton Cap Viaduct.

A family fish in the river upstream of Newton Cap Viaduct.

Flowering gorse bushes surround the modern Jubilee Bridge.

An overhanging tree frames this view of the 1995 Page Bank Bridge.

Looking upstream to Croxdale Viaduct through a wooded riverbank.

Croxdale Viaduct skirts a cornfield on its way north to Tyneside.

The old stone Sunderland Bridge at Croxdale viewed from the east.

Croxdale's road bridge of 1924.

The reinforced concrete Baths Bridge of 1962 – the third footbridge on this site.

Looking upstream to New Elvet Bridge.

This downstream shot of New Elvet Bridge includes a view of the Castle and Cathedral.

Old Elvet Bridge looking to the south with Brown's Boatyard to the right.

The high level footbridge of Kingsgate which was erected in 1963.

Late afternoon sun provides the lighting for this tranquil view of Prebends Bridge.

Looking upstream to Prebends Bridge which was built between 1772 and 1778.

The Castle and Cathedral provide a backdrop for Framwellgate Bridge.

Framwellgate Bridge was Durham's first permanent river crossing.

The sun sets behind an illuminated Penny Ferry Bridge.

The abandoned Belmont Viaduct in Kepier Woods.

The Toll Bridge at Finchale Priory which was erected in 1937.

The exposed roots of a tree add interest to this view of the Toll Bridge at Finchale.

Looking downstream to the lattice iron girders of Cocken Bridge.

Members of Chester-le-Street's Sea Cadet Corps prepare to take to the water near the New Lumley Bridge.

The surviving abutments of Old Lumley Bridge. The spire of St Mary's and St Cuthbert's Church is visible to the right.

The 15th century Chester New Bridge now provides entry into the Lambton Estate.

Lamb Bridge on the Lambton Estate as viewed from the south.

The single graceful arch of Lamb Bridge.

Dappled sun on a line of silver birch trees enhances this summer view of Fatfield or Penshaw Bridge.

Penshaw Monument is framed by the cross girders of Fatfield or Penshaw Bridge.

Early evening sunshine provides the lighting for this downstream shot of Victoria Viaduct.

A giant hogweed dominates the foreground of this upstream view of Victoria Viaduct.

Smoke from a fire adds interest to this spring photograph of Victoria Viaduct.

Coxgreen Footbridge on a summer's day. Inset: A reminder that the Barmston Ferry once operated here.

Looking upstream to the A19 Hylton Road Bridge from Barons Quay.

Early morning sunshine lights up this view of the Queen Alexandra Bridge.

A Metro train crosses Sunderland's hog back rail bridge of 1879.

The bridges of Sunderland are reflected on a peaceful river in this atmospheric photograph.

Wearmouth's rail and road bridge as viewed from St Mary's car park.

A fishing boat berths at the Fish Quay and looks upstream to the bridges at Sunderland.

The Wearmouth Bridges on a sunny autumn morning.